TRIGONOMETRY

ADDISON–WESLEY MATHEMATICS SERIES

Eric Reissner, *Consulting Editor*

TRIGONOMETRY

ELBRIDGE P. VANCE

Oberlin College

1954

ADDISON–WESLEY PUBLISHING COMPANY, INC.

CAMBRIDGE 42, MASS.

PREFACE

A course in trigonometry should serve two classes of students: (1) those liberal arts students who elect a small amount of mathematics and who wish to obtain an insight into mathematics as it is applied in the world today, and (2) those who wish to prepare themselves for further study in mathematics and other physical sciences. We would be unfair to both groups of students if we did not permit them to acquire some feeling for mathematical thought and processes in addition to actual course content. It was with this in mind that the author wrote the present book.

The choice of topics, the proportionate time spent on each, and the logical treatment throughout are intended to emphasize the modern point of view. A brief discussion of the different number systems and the one-dimensional coordinate system is basic for the introduction of the rectangular coordinate system. The definitions of the circular functions in terms of this coordinate system, a feature which distinguishes this text from many, is the basic unifying link between trigonometry and analytic geometry, and enables the author to employ many simpler, more direct methods. The analytic rather than the computational part of trigonometry has been emphasized, although the latter has been included. Both degree and radian measure of angles are introduced at the beginning, and are treated together thereafter.

Certain topics not usually found in trigonometry books are included. The discussion of the circular functions of $\pi/5$ (Article 2-6), the comments about circular function tables and the material involving special methods for small angles (Article 4-1), the approach, by means of ordered pairs, to the study of complex numbers (Chapter 7), and the insight into some of the applications of the circular functions in the description of many periodic phenomena (Chapter 8) are of this type.

It was the aim of the author to write a versatile text, which could be used for any purpose from a half-semester course in the bare essentials to a full semester course in Trigonometry and allied subjects. Starred articles and chapters may be omitted without loss of continuity. Also, Chapter 4 may be postponed, for no material which follows depends on this chapter.

v

The Appendix includes a table of powers and roots and four-place tables of circular functions, logarithms, and the logarithms of the circular functions, together with an explanation of the tables and a brief discussion of the use of logarithms for computational purposes and interpolation. All of the answers for the exercises in the Appendix are included in the Answer section. For the problems throughout the text, only the odd-numbered answers are given.

The author is grateful to Professor Burton W. Jones of the University of Colorado, Professor D. R. Morrison of Tulane University, and Professor Robert R. Stoll of Oberlin College for their many helpful suggestions, and to the staff of Addison-Wesley for their valuable assistance.

E.P.V.

May, 1954

CONTENTS

Starred sections may be omitted without loss of continuity.

CHAPTER 1

NUMBERS AND COORDINATE SYSTEMS

The basic quantitative procedures of science involve counting and measurement. Counting is the act that leads to the characterization of a collection of objects by a number. Measurement is the act that leads to the assignment of a number to a property of an object. Both counting and measurement are far from simple concepts, and both have been the subject of many studies in the field of scientific methodology. The important thing for us in the present study is the fact that both counting and measurement lead to numbers, and through the use of numbers it is possible to obtain much insight into the workings of nature. Although a thorough study of our number system is beyond the scope of this book, we shall begin with the classification of the various types of numbers and then, using them, we shall introduce certain basic notions which are helpful in the presentation of an analytic study of trigonometry.

1–1 Numbers. The first numbers encountered by everyone are the counting or natural numbers 1, 2, 3, $\cdots$. We refer to these as the set of *positive integers*. These numbers, together with the *negative integers*, -1, -2, -3, $\cdots$, and the zero integer 0, are called the *set of integers*. When any two integers are added, subtracted, or multiplied, the result is an integer. That is, if a and b are integers, $a + b$, $a - b$, and ab are also integers. Moreover, the operations of addition and multiplication on the integers satisfy the following well-known and important laws:

$$a + b = b + a,$$

$$ab = ba,$$

$$a + (b + c) = (a + b) + c, \qquad (1\text{--}1)$$

$$a(bc) = (ab)c,$$

$$a(b + c) = ab + ac.$$

Next, in forming quotients of integers, the rational numbers are introduced. If a is any integer and b is any integer different from

1

zero, then a/b is defined as the number c which, when multiplied by b, gives a. That is, c is defined by the equation $cb = a$. Fractions of the form $a/0$ are not defined. We therefore say that $a/0$ does not exist, and division by zero is not permitted. Any number which we can express as the quotient or ratio of two integers (excluding division by zero) is called a *rational number*, and the entire set of all such quotients is called the *set of rational numbers*. The numbers $5/3$, $-13/2$, 3, and 1.414 are rational numbers. Any integer n, such as 3, is a rational number, since $n = n/1$. The number 1.414, which is an approximation for $\sqrt{2}$, is a rational number, since

$$1.414 = \frac{1414}{1000}.$$

Any rational number may be written as a decimal and, in fact, one way of identifying such a number is by its decimal expansion, which either terminates or is periodic.*

There are many numbers expressible as unending decimals which are not rational. It has been shown that the numbers $\sqrt{2}$, π (the ratio of the circumference of any circle to its diameter), and e (the base for logarithms used in calculus) cannot be expressed as the quotient of two integers and yet can be written as unending decimals. The entire set of numbers expressible as unending decimals is called the *set of real numbers*, and those in this set which are not rational form the *set of irrational numbers*.† Any irrational number, however, can be approximated by rational numbers. For example, the rational number approximation for $\sqrt{2}$, correct to three decimal places, is 1.414. The rational number 22/7 is a common approximation for π, while a more accurate one is 3.1416. The sum, difference, product, or quotient (division by other than zero) of any two real numbers is a real number. Moreover, the real numbers satisfy the laws stated in equations (1–1).

Although we shall deal primarily with real numbers in this book, there are other types of numbers which result from generalizations or extensions of the real numbers. The *set of complex numbers* is one

---

* Periodic in this sense means that the digits repeat either from the beginning ($.161616\cdots$), or after a certain stage ($3.2454545\cdots$).

† For a careful definition of irrational number, see R. Dedekind, *Essays on the Theory of Numbers, I: Continuity and Irrational Numbers.* Authorized translation by W. W. Beman. Chicago: Open Court Publishing Company, 1909.

such type and will be discussed in Chapter 7. Throughout this book, unless otherwise stated, all numbers will be considered as belonging to the set of real numbers.

1–2 A one-dimensional coordinate system. The method of associating numbers with points on a line is of considerable help in mathematics and has resulted in great progress in the application of mathematics to science. Any scale which measures quantities, such as a yardstick or thermometer, makes use of an association of this kind. To each numerical value assumed by the physical quantity there corresponds a position on the scale, and to each position on the scale there corresponds a number. Such a correspondence establishes a coordinate system. The simplest and most useful coordinate system in one dimension employs this one-to-one correspondence between the real numbers and the points on a straight line. Let us consider such a system.

On a fixed straight line of reference of unlimited length, we choose any point O, called the *origin*, and lay off equal divisions* of arbitrary length in both directions from O (see Fig. 1–1). We now associate zero with the origin, the positive integers with the successive points on one side, and the negative integers with the successive points on the other. The usual convention on such a horizontal line is to consider the integers to the right as positive and those to the left as negative.

The point associated with any rational number can be determined by the simple geometric construction used to divide any line segment into b equal parts. Thus the number $\frac{3}{4}$ is represented by a point three-fourths of the way from 0 to the point identified with 1. Also, $-1\frac{3}{8}$ is represented by a point at a distance $1\frac{3}{8}$ units to the left of 0.

The points associated with some of the irrational numbers may also be found by geometric construction. For example, the point associated with $\sqrt{2}$ may be located, because $\sqrt{2}$ is the hypotenuse

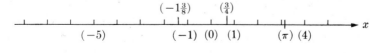

FIGURE 1–1

* There are systems where the subdivisions are not equal. Consider the slide rule scale.

of an isosceles right triangle, with each leg one unit in length. Although this type of geometric construction is not possible for all real numbers, we shall assume that the correspondence can be extended to all real numbers. This is done by associating every line segment with a real number which represents its length. Thus to each real number we have associated one point on the line and, conversely, to each point on the line there is associated one real number.

The *coordinate* of a point is defined to be the number associated with that point. It is written (x), and will be referred to as "the point x."

There are certain properties of this sytem which we should observe. It gives us a graphic interpretation of the relative magnitude of numbers. Thus $5 > 3$ (read 5 is greater than 3)* corresponds to the fact that (5) lies to the right of (3), while $-5 < -3$ (read -5 is less than -3) corresponds to the fact that (-5) is to the left of (-3). The notation $x < y < z$ indicates that y is greater than x but less than z.

An expression for the distance between any two points in this system is important and useful. We need only to subtract the coordinate of the left-hand point from the coordinate of the right-hand point. Thus, if $x_1 < x_2$, the distance between (x_1) and (x_2) is $x_2 - x_1$, but if $x_2 < x_1$, the distance must be $x_1 - x_2$, since we wish to have the distance always positive. We can avoid the inconvenience of having to distinguish between the two points by employing the notion of absolute value.

The absolute value of x, denoted by $|x|$, indicates its size or magnitude without regard to its sign. For example, $|3| = 3$, and $|-3| = 3$. Specifically, the *absolute value* of a number x is defined as

$$|x| = \begin{cases} x \text{ if } x > 0, \\ -x \text{ if } x < 0, \\ 0 \text{ if } x = 0. \end{cases} \tag{1-2}$$

In this connection we should recall the definition of the square root sign, $\sqrt{\ }$. For any positive number a, $\sqrt{a}$ denotes the positive square root of a; that is, for any real number x, x^2 is positive (or zero if $x = 0$) and

* If x and y are any two real numbers, by definition,
$\quad x > y$ is equivalent to $x - y$ is positive,
$\quad x < y$ is equivalent to $x - y$ is negative.

$$\sqrt{x^2} = \begin{cases} x \text{ if } x > 0, \\ -x \text{ if } x < 0, \\ 0 \text{ if } x = 0. \end{cases} \qquad (1\text{-}3)$$

Thus $\sqrt{7^2} = 7$, and $\sqrt{(-7)^2} = -(-7) = 7$. Since (1-2) and (1-3) define the same values, either expression can be used to indicate absolute value.

We are now able to give the general expression for the distance between any two points P_1 and P_2 with coordinates (x_1) and (x_2):

$$d = \overline{P_1 P_2} = |x_1 - x_2| = \sqrt{(x_1 - x_2)^2}. \qquad (1\text{-}4)$$

For example, the distance between the two points (5) and (-3) is given either by the expression

$$d = \sqrt{[5 - (-3)]^2} = 8,$$

or the expression

$$d = \sqrt{(-3 - 5)^2} = 8.$$

Problems

1. Arrange the following numbers in ascending order of magnitude, and plot them on a linear coordinate system such as that of Fig. 1-1: 2.3, 0.333, 2^3, $\sqrt{4}$, 1/3, -5, -1, 0, -6.5.

2. Choose two negative numbers, a and b, such that $a > b$. Show that $a - b$ is a positive number.

3. State in words the geometrical interpretation of the following:

(a) $a < b$

(b) $a < 2$

(c) $a > b$

(d) $a > b > c$

(e) $a - b = 1$

(f) $3.14 < \pi < 3.15$

(g) $1.41 < \sqrt{2} < 1.42$

(h) $|5 - 2| > |1 - 3|$

(i) $|a - b| > 0$

(j) $|x - 2| < 3$

(k) $|x - 1| > 4$

(l) $-1 < x < 1$

4. If the coordinates of two points, P_1 and P_2, on a line are (2) and (8) respectively, show that the coordinate of the mid-point of the segment $P_1 P_2$ is (5).

5. Find the coordinate of the mid-point of the line joining (4) and (-4), (3) and (-5), (-1.7) and (3.7), $(\sqrt{2})$ and $(\sqrt{3})$, (x_1) and (x_2).

6. Solve the following equations for x:

(a) $x = |10|$

(b) $x = |2 - 5|$

(c) $x = \sqrt{3^2}$

(d) $x = \sqrt{(-4)^2}$

(e) $x = |-3/2|$ (f) $x = \sqrt{(-1)^2}$

(g) $x = |1/3 - 5/3|$ (h) $x = |1/3| + |-5/3|$

7. Solve the following equations for all possible values of x:

(a) $|x| = 2$ (b) $|x| = \sqrt{5}$

(c) $\sqrt{x^2} = 3$ (d) $\sqrt{x^2} = 1/4$

(e) $|x - 2| = 5$ (f) $|x - 4| = 0$

(g) $|3 - x| = 6$ (h) $\sqrt{(x - 1)^2} = 5$

(i) $\sqrt{(2 - x)^2} = 4$ (j) $|x - 2| = -3$

(k) $\sqrt{(x - 4)^2} = -1$ (l) $\sqrt{(x - 5)^2} = 3$

8. Recall from plane geometry that a circle is the locus (totality) of points at a given distance from a given point, where the distance is called the radius and the given point is called the center. In this geometry of one dimension, how many points are at a given distance from a fixed point? Of how many points would a "circle" consist?

9. If (1) is a given point, and 2 a given distance, explain how $|x - 1| = 2$ would be the condition that any point (x) must be 2 units distant from (1). This is the condition that the point (x) lie on the "circle" with center (1) and radius 2, and is called the equation of the "circle."

10. In terms of "circles in one dimension," give the geometric significance of each of the equations in Problem 7.

11. Give the equation of a "circle in one dimension" with its center at the point (a) and of radius r.

1–3 A two-dimensional coordinate system. In the last article we observed a useful coordinate system in one dimension which not only enabled us to view the relative magnitudes of numbers in a graphic way, but also allowed us to represent differences in magnitude by the use of distance. But for many purposes this is not enough. One of the more important concepts in mathematics is the study of the relation or dependence of two sets of numbers. Since the corresponding values of two such related sets might be considered as pairs of numbers, any system which produces an association between a point and a pair of numbers would be most advantageous in studying such a relationship. This is easily accomplished in two dimensions.

The most frequently used system that sets up an association between each point in a plane and a pair of real numbers is the rectangular cartesian system of coordinates. In 1637 René Descartes, a French mathematician and philosopher, discovered this method of

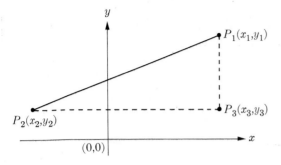

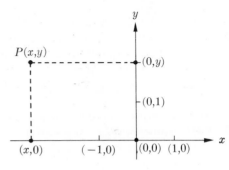

FIGURE 1–4

FIGURE 1–2

two points $P_1(x_1,y_1)$ and $P_2(x_2,y_2)$, where the same unit lengths are used on both axes, we make use of the famous theorem of Pythagoras. Considering $P_1(x_1,y_1)$ and $P_2(x_2,y_2)$ as any two points in the plane, construct a right triangle, as in Fig. 1–4, with P_1P_2 the hypotenuse, and the two legs parallel to the axes.   Call their point of intersection, where the right angle is formed, $P_3(x_3,y_3)$.   Since $x_3 = x_1$ and $y_3 = y_2$, the distance between P_2 and P_3 is

$$P_2P_3 = \sqrt{(x_1 - x_2)^2}$$

and the distance between P_1 and P_3 is

$$P_1P_3 = \sqrt{(y_1 - y_2)^2}.$$

Recalling the theorem of Pythagoras, which states

$$\overline{P_1P_2}^2 = \overline{P_2P_3}^2 + \overline{P_1P_3}^2,$$

we obtain

$$\overline{P_1P_2}^2 = (x_1 - x_2)^2 + (y_1 - y_2)^2.$$

This result may be written:

$$d = P_1P_2 = \sqrt{(x_1 - x_2)^2 + (y_1 - y_2)^2}. \qquad (1-5)$$

EXAMPLE 1.   The distance between the points $P_1(-4,2)$ and $P_2(3,-1)$ is

$$P_1P_2 = \sqrt{[3 - (-4)]^2 + (-1 - 2)^2}$$

$$= \sqrt{58}.$$

associating numbers with points, and by this unifying of algebra and geometry, great progress in mathematics and the application of mathematics in science was made possible.

Let us construct two perpendicular straight lines and, for convenience, let one of them be horizontal.   We shall call these *coordinate axes*.   Using the point of intersection as the *origin O*, set up on each line a one-dimensional system.   Ordinarily the same unit of length is used on both lines, although in some cases it is convenient to do otherwise.   We now denote by the symbol $(x,0)$ the point on the horizontal line corresponding to the number x in its one-dimensional system.   Similarly, we denote the point on the vertical line corresponding to the number y in its one-dimensional system by the symbol $(0,y)$.   The horizontal line is called the *x-axis* or *axis of abscissas*, while the vertical line is referred to as the *y-axis* or *axis of ordinates*.   As is customary, the point on the y-axis $(0,y)$ is above the x-axis when y is positive.

In this reference system of axes, shown in Fig. 1–2, consider any pair of values of x and y, say x_1 and y_1.   To find the point corresponding to this pair of values, we draw lines parallel to the axes through the point $(x_1,0)$ on the x-axis and the point $(0,y_1)$ on the y-axis.   These lines intersect at a point P, a distance x_1 from the y-axis (to the right or left, depending upon whether x_1 is positive or negative) and a distance y_1 from the x-axis (above or below, depending upon whether y_1 is positive or negative).   This point P, determined by the pair of values x_1 and y_1, is denoted by the symbol (x_1,y_1), where x_1 and y_1 are called the *coordinates* of P.   As might be expected, the value x is called the *abscissa* of P and the y-value is called its *ordinate*.   Clearly, there is only one point determined by any pair of values (x,y).   Conversely, for each point there is only one pair of values (x,y), for the point has unique directed distances from the axes.   Thus the one-to-one correspondence is established between all the points in the plane and the set of all number pairs (x,y).

The two coordinate axes divide the plane into four parts, called the *first*, *second*, *third*, and *fourth quadrants*. It is helpful to verify that the coordinates of points located in the different quadrants have the signs shown in the table:

Quadrants	abscissa	ordinate
I	+	+
II	−	+
III	−	−
IV	+	−

Let us illustrate in Fig. 1–3 the plotting of several points.

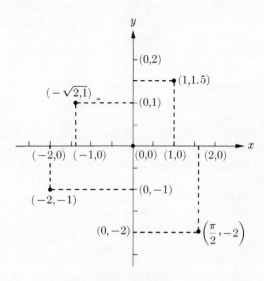

FIGURE 1–3

PROBLEMS

1. Plot the following points:
   (a) with abscissa 4 and ordinate 3,
   (b) $(4,-3)$,
   (c) with $x = -4$ and $y = 3$.

2. Plot the following points:
   (a) $(2,6)$, $(-1,4)$, $(3,-2)$, $(-1,-3)$;
   (b) $(4,0)$, $(-4,0)$, $(0,4)$, $(0,-4)$, $(0,0)$.

3. What are the coordinates of a point (a) three units to th y-axis, and two above the x-axis?   (b) four units to the left of th six above the x-axis?   (c) five units to the right of the y-axis, or

4. (a) What is the abscissa of any point on the y-axis?   (b) ordinate of any point on the x-axis?

5. Without plotting, indicate the quadrant in which each of the points lies: $(-1,2)$, $(2,-4)$, $(-3,-7)$, $(4,6)$, $(-5,2)$, $(28,-2)$.

6. (a) Give the coordinates of four points which are the verti rectangle.   (b) Give the coordinates of three points which are the ve a right triangle.   (c) Give the coordinates of four points on a circle w center at $(2,3)$ and of radius 4.

7. In each of the following, three vertices of a parallelogram are g Give the three possible sets of coordinates for the fourth vertex:
   (a) $(0,0)$, $(2,4)$, and $(6,0)$;
   (b) $(-2,1)$, $(1,2)$, and $(0,-3)$.

8. Three vertices of a parallelogram are (a,b), $(0,0)$, and $(c,0)$.   What a the possible coordinates of the fourth vertex?

9. Indicate in a rectangular coordinate system the location of the set o all the points (x,y) which satisfy the following conditions:

(a) $x = 2$	(b) $y = -3$
(c) $x > 2$	(d) $y > 4$
(e) $x < -1$	(f) $x = y$
(g) $x > 2$ $\quad y = 3$	(h) $x > y$
(i) $x < y$	(j) $x > 2$ $\quad y < 4$
(k) $x = 2$ $\quad y < -1$	(l) $x = 2$ $\quad y = 3$

1–4 The distance formula. We are now prepared to obtain a formula which has many applications in the material dealt with in this book.   To obtain an expression for the distance d between any

EXAMPLE 2.   The distance between the origin $(0,0)$ and any point (x,y) is

$$d = \sqrt{(x-0)^2 + (y-0)^2}$$
$$= \sqrt{x^2 + y^2}.$$

EXAMPLE 3.   The triangle with the points $P_1(-5,-1)$, $P_2(2,3)$, and $P_3(3,-2)$ as vertices forms an isosceles triangle.

$$P_1P_2 = \sqrt{(-5-2)^2 + (-1-3)^2}$$
$$= \sqrt{49+16} = \sqrt{65}.$$
$$P_1P_3 = \sqrt{(-5-3)^2 + (-1+2)^2}$$
$$= \sqrt{64+1} = \sqrt{65}.$$

PROBLEMS

In each of the following exercises draw the figure on coordinate paper.

1. Find the distance between the given points:

(a) $(3,2)$ and $(6,7)$ (b) $(-4,3)$ and $(5,-2)$

(c) $(5/2,-3/4)$ and $(7/4,-3/2)$ (d) $(0,0)$ and $(5,-12)$

(e) $(-3,7)$ and $(5,7)$ (f) $(-1,3)$ and (x,y)

2. By proving that two sides of the triangle are equal, show that the triangle whose vertices are $(2,1)$, $(5,5)$, and $(-2,4)$ is an isosceles triangle.

3. Show that the points $(8,1)$, $(-6,-7)$, and $(2,7)$ are the vertices of an isosceles triangle.

4. Show that the points $(6,1)$, $(5,6)$, $(-4,3)$, and $(-3,-2)$ are the vertices of a parallelogram.

5. Prove that the points $(2,3)$, $(-4,-3)$, and $(6,-1)$ are the vertices of a right triangle.   Notice that we must use the converse of the theorem of Pythagoras to prove this.

6. Show that the points $(12,9)$, $(20,-6)$, $(5,-14)$, and $(-3,1)$ are the vertices of a square.   What is the length of a diagonal?

7. Test algebraically to see whether or not the following triples of points are collinear (lie on the same line): $(6,2)$, $(1,1)$, $(-4,0)$; $(-6,5)$, $(3,-10)$, $(-2,-2)$.

8. Find the point on the y-axis which is equidistant from the points $(-4,4)$ and $(4,10)$.

9. If two vertices of an equilateral triangle are $(-4,-3)$ and $(4,1)$, find the remaining vertex.

10. Find those points whose ordinates are -5 and whose distance from the origin is 13.

11. Draw the square whose diagonals lie along the coordinate axes and the length of whose side is a. What are the coordinates of the four vertices?

12. If a circle had its center at the point $(2,3)$ and passed through $(8,-5)$, what would be its radius? Would it pass through $(-6,9)$?

13. Consider the circle with its center at the origin and with a radius of 1. Through which of the following points does it pass: $(1,0)$, $(0,-1)$, $(1,1)$, $(1/\sqrt{2}, 1/\sqrt{2})$, $(1/2, 1/2)$, $(-1/2, \sqrt{3}/2)$?

14. By giving the expression for the distance between the origin and the point (x,y), and equating this distance to 1, we have stated the algebraic condition on x and y which must be satisfied by the coordinates of any point (x,y) lying on the circle whose center is $(0,0)$ and whose radius is 1. Show that this condition, when simplified, becomes $x^2 + y^2 = 1$. This is called the equation of the unit circle in the plane.

15. If a point lies on a curve, its coordinates must satisfy the equation representing that curve. Check the results of Problem 13 by determining whether the coordinates of the points satisfy the equation of the unit circle obtained in Problem 14, namely, $x^2 + y^2 = 1$.

1-5 The circle and arc length. In any rectangular coordinate system a geometric figure, locus, or curve, such as a circle, is considered as a set of points. The coordinates of each point in this set satisfy the equation of this curve and, conversely, if the coordinates of any point satisfy this equation, the point must lie on the curve. Thus an *equation of any curve* is a statement of the condition which the coordinates of each of the points of the curve, and only these points, must satisfy.

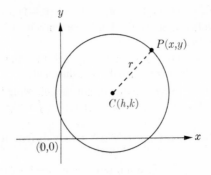

FIGURE 1-5

We recall the definition of a *circle* as the locus (totality) of points in the plane which are at a constant distance from a fixed point. Using the distance formula, it is now possible to obtain the general equation of a circle.

With $C(h,k)$ as the center and r as the radius (Fig. 1–5), the condition that any point $P(x,y)$ lying on the circle must satisfy is

$$CP = r,$$

which is the same as having the coordinates of P satisfy

$$\sqrt{(x-h)^2 + (y-k)^2} = r$$

from Eq. (1–5). Conversely, if $CP = r$, then P is on the circle. We therefore have

$$(x-h)^2 + (y-k)^2 = r^2, \tag{1–6}$$

which is the general equation of a circle with center (h,k) and with radius r.

EXAMPLE 1. An equation of the circle with its center at $(2,-3)$ and radius 4 is

$$(x-2)^2 + (y+3)^2 = 16.$$

EXAMPLE 2. An equation of the circle with its center at the origin and a radius of 1 is

$$(x-0)^2 + (y-0)^2 = 1,$$

or

$$x^2 + y^2 = 1.$$

This is called an equation of the unit circle, an important special case in our study. Recall Problem 14 of the last section.

We are interested not only in the equation of a circle, but also in the notion of length of portions of its circumference. The length of a circular arc is most useful in discussing and measuring angles.

By considering a circular arc $\overset{\frown}{AB}$, as in Fig. 1–6, it is possible to assign to this arc $\overset{\frown}{AB}$ a length s, although it is impossible to measure the length directly. By denoting several points on $\overset{\frown}{AB}$ by C, D, and so on, the length of the polygonal line joining these points is the

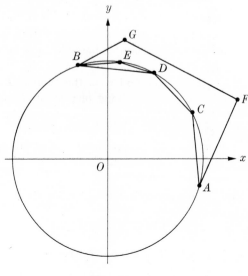

FIGURE 1–6

sum of the lengths of the appropriate chords, obtained by using formula (1–5).

If we now consider other points on the arc $\overset{\frown}{AB}$, such as E, the new polygonal line $ACDEB$ has a greater length than $ACDB$, since

$$BD < DE + EB.$$

Continuing this process of inserting points, we shall obtain polygonal lines whose lengths are greater than the preceding ones. However, the length of our polygonal line cannot become infinite, for it can be shown that the length of any line obtained in this way is always less than the length of any polygonal line which joins A and B outside the circle, such as $AFGB$. Therefore, we have a number of polygonal lines, each with a length greater than the last, and yet smaller than a fixed number. If the number of chords is increased, and their lengths become arbitrarily close to zero, it can be shown that the length of this polygonal line will approach a definite value. This definite value, s, is called the *arc length* of $\overset{\frown}{AB}$.

EXAMPLE. The circumference or arc length of the entire circle with radius r is equal to $2\pi r$, or approximately 6.28 times the radius.

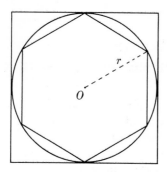

FIGURE 1–7

Compare this with the two regular geometric figures shown in Fig. 1–7. Since the inscribed hexagon has a perimeter of $6r$ and the circumscribed square has a perimeter of $8r$, the inequality $6r < 2\pi r < 8r$ would be expected.

PROBLEMS

1. Write an equation of the following circles:
   (a) center at $(3,1)$ and radius 5,
   (b) center at $(4,-2)$ and radius 3,
   (c) center at $(-1,3)$ tangent to the x-axis,
   (d) center at $(2,-4)$ and passing through $(5,-8)$.

2. Write an equation of the circle with its center at the origin and radius r.

3. Describe the set of points (x,y) which satisfy:
   (a) $(x-1)^2 + (y-1)^2 \leq 1$,
   (b) $(x-2)^2 + (y+3)^2 \geq 4$,
   (c) $(x-3)^2 + (y+1)^2 = 0$.

4. What is the length of the perimeter of the square inscribed in a circle of radius r?

5. Determine the length of the perimeter of the regular hexagon circumscribed about a circle of radius r.

6. Expressing your answer in terms of π, what is the length of the circumference of the unit circle (a circle with a radius of 1)? What is the length of an arc one-fourth the distance around the circle? What is the length of an arc one-sixth the distance around the circle?

CHAPTER 2
THE CIRCULAR FUNCTIONS

2-1 Trigonometry. In about 1600 A.D. Bartholomaus Pitiscus, a professor of mathematics at Heidelberg, wrote the first textbook to bear the title of *Trigonometry*. What he had in mind was exactly what the name implies: triangle measurement. Actually, however, trigonometry had its origin in early historical times. This was a part of the attempt to study and describe the celestial sphere in which the sun, moon, and stars were supposed to move. The two most prominent men interested in these developments were the Greek astronomers, Hipparchus of Nicaea (Second Century B.C.) and Claudius Ptolemy (Second Century A.D.). As a consequence, one often gains the impression that the principle, if not the sole application, of trigonometry is the solving of triangles, and thus that the application of trigonometry lies in the fields of astronomy, navigation, and surveying. This may have been true 2000 or even 400 years ago, but it is certainly not the case today.

With the development of trigonometry, the general study of the circular functions has progressed. In fact, we now define trigonometry as that branch of mathematics which is concerned with the properties and applications of the circular or trigonometric functions. Since these functions are defined at any elementary level in terms of angles, the notion of angle is an important one.

2-2 Angles. In geometry an angle has usually been defined as the configuration consisting of two half-lines (rays) radiating from a point. However, in trigonometry we generalize this definition by stating that an angle thus defined by two half-lines has a measure which corresponds to the amount of rotation required to move a ray from the position of one of these lines to the other. Consider Fig. 2–1, with the two lines m and n intersecting at O and lying in a plane perpendicular to our line of vision. If we consider m as the *initial side* and n as the *terminal side* of the angle with O as its vertex, there are two possible directions of rotation of the initial side m. The angle is said to be *positive* if the rotation is counterclockwise, but *negative* if clockwise. A curved arrow will indicate the direction of rotation.

16

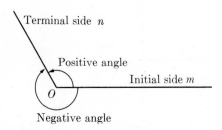

FIGURE 2–1

Let us now consider a ray m which issues from the origin of a rectangular coordinate system and coincides with the positive x-axis (Fig. 2–2). As this ray rotates, any point P on m will trace out part or all of the circumference of a circle of radius OP. In fact, the circumference may be traced several times. After the rotation, OP will be in some position OP', where the circular arc $\overparen{PP'}$, denoted by s, may be used to measure the angle POP'. An angle such as POP' is said to be in *standard position,* and to be in the quadrant in which its terminal side OP' is located.

The most logical units for measuring the magnitude of an angle would seem to be the number of revolutions due to the rotation from the initial to the terminal side of the angle. Since the number of revolutions of any angle is determined by the ratio of the intercepted

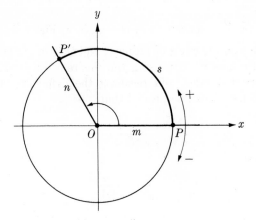

FIGURE 2–2

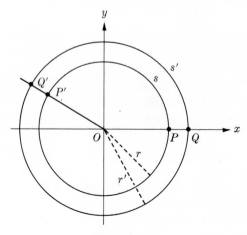

FIGURE 2–3

circular arc length s to the circumference of the circle, we define
the magnitude of an angle in revolutions as

$$\text{Angle* in revolutions} = \frac{s}{2\pi r}. \qquad (2\text{--}1)$$

For example, if P traces out an arc one-half the circumference,
the corresponding angle is one of one-half a revolution. Likewise,
if the arc is twice the circumference, the angle measure is two
revolutions.

Consider the two concentric circles at O, in Fig. 2–3, with $\overset{\frown}{PP'}$ an
arc of length s on the circle of radius r, and $\overset{\frown}{QQ'}$ an arc of length s' on
the circle of radius r'. By using the theorem that similar triangles
have proportional sides, and recalling the definition of arc length
from Article 1–6, it can be proved that

$$\frac{s'}{r'} = \frac{s}{r},$$

and, therefore,

$$\frac{s'}{2\pi r'} = \frac{s}{2\pi r}.$$

---

* Since we so frequently are considering angles in terms of their magnitudes, we use the word "angle" in place of "measure of angle."

The magnitude of any angle is thus independent of the length of its initial or terminal side.

Although the use of revolutions is the most natural method for measuring angles, there are other more convenient systems.

The system most commonly used in elementary work such as surveying and navigation is the *Sexagesimal System*, in which the degree* is the fundamental unit. In this system one revolution = 360°, 1° = 60′ (minutes), and 1′ = 60″ (seconds). Thus:

$$\text{Angle in degrees} = (\text{revolutions}) \, (360°). \qquad (2\text{–}2)$$

For example, one-half a revolution is 180°, or an angle of two revolutions is 720°.

The other important system used in calculus and other more advanced mathematics is the *Radian System*. Recalling that the circumference of the unit circle is 2π, we define one revolution to be 2π radians and have

$$\text{Angle in radians} = (\text{revolutions}) \, (2\pi). \qquad (2\text{–}3)$$

For example, one-half a revolution is π radians, or an angle of two revolutions is 4π radians. When no unit of measure is designated, radian measure is understood.

We have two immediate results from these definitions. Solving (2–2) and (2–3) for (revolutions) and equating, we find the relationship between an angle expressed in degrees and radians to be

$$\frac{\text{Angle in degrees}}{360°} = \frac{\text{Angle in radians}}{2\pi}. \qquad (2\text{–}4)$$

EXAMPLE 1. An angle of 45° is equal to

$$\frac{45°}{360°} \, 2\pi = \frac{\pi}{4} \text{ radians.}$$

EXAMPLE 2. An angle of $5\pi/6$ radians is equal to

$$\left(\frac{5\pi/6}{2\pi}\right) 360° = 150°.$$

---

* The origin of the use of the degree for measurement is discussed by O. Neugebauer in *Studies of the History of Science*. Philadelphia: University of Pennsylvania Press, 1941. Bicentennial Conference. Chapter on Ancient Astronomy, p. 16.

EXAMPLE 3.   To express an angle of one radian in degrees, the same method is used:

$$1 \text{ radian} = \frac{1}{2\pi}\, 360° = \frac{360°}{2\pi} = 57°18' \text{ (approximately).} \quad (2\text{--}5)$$

Similarly, for an angle of one degree,

$$1° = 2\pi\left(\frac{\text{-}1°}{360°}\right) = .01745 \text{ radian (approximately).} \quad (2\text{--}6)$$

EXAMPLE 4.   Transform an angle of 194°23′ to radian measure.

Solution. In Table I, the angles are given in both degrees and radians. We may use this table to change from one system to the other. Since

$$194°23' = 180° + 14°23',$$

we work with 14°23′.

$$14°20' = .2502 \text{ radian,}$$

and

$$14°30' = .2531 \text{ radian.}$$

By interpolation,* we get

$$14°23' = .2511 \text{ radian.}$$

Therefore

$$194°23' = (\pi + .2511) \text{ radians}$$
$$= 3.3927 \text{ radians (approximately).}$$

The second result shows the advantage of the radian system in measuring angles. Writing (2–3) with the substitution from (2–1), we have

$$\text{Angle in radians} = \frac{s}{2\pi r}\,(2\pi) = \frac{s}{r}.$$

Therefore the length of the circular arc s cut by a central angle θ (measured in radians) in a circle of radius r is given by

$$s = r\theta. \quad (2\text{--}7)$$

---

* Interpolation is explained in some detail in the Appendix.

EXAMPLE. A circle has a radius of 40 inches. (a) How long is the arc subtended by a central angle of 36°?

Solution. Since the number of radians corresponding to 36° is $\pi/5$,

$$s = 40\left(\frac{\pi}{5}\right) = 8\pi \text{ inches.}$$

Using an approximation for π, this answer can be written to any desired degree of accuracy.

(b) How large is the central angle that subtends an arc of 15 inches?

Solution. Again using $s = r\theta$, $15 = 40\theta$ or $\theta = \frac{3}{8}$ radian. If the result is desired in degrees, we merely change $\frac{3}{8}$ radian into degrees, obtaining 21°30′.

PROBLEMS

1. In a rectangular coordinate system, locate the following angles in standard position, showing the initial and terminal sides. Use a curved arrow to indicate the direction in which the angle is measured.

(a) 1/4 rev.   (b) −3/4 rev.   (c) 3 rev.   (d) 3/8 rev.
(e) −1/6 rev.   (f) −5/4 rev.   (g) 5/6 rev.   (h) −5/3 rev.

2. Repeat Problem 1 for the following angles expressed in degrees:

(a) 45°   (b) 135°   (c) −225°   (d) −300°
(e) 240°   (f) 450°   (g) 720°   (h) −120°

3. Repeat Problem 1 for the following angles expressed in radians:

(a) $\pi/6$ (b) $2\pi/3$ (c) $\pi/4$ (d) $4\pi/9$
(e) $-3\pi/2$ (f) $-5\pi/6$ (g) $5\pi/12$ (h) -5π

4. Express the angles given in Problems 1 and 2 in radian measure, leaving the answer in terms of π.

5. Express the angles given in Problems 2 and 3 in revolutions.

6. Express the angles given in Problems 1 and 3 in degrees.

7. Transform the following angles to radians, using Table I if needed, and giving the answer to four decimal places.

(a) 27°   (b) 156°20′   (c) 47°
(d) 189°32′   (e) 253°10′   (f) −378°49′

8. Transform the following angles to degrees and minutes, using Table I if needed, and giving the answer to the nearest minute.

(a) $\pi/8$ (b) $-2\pi/13$ (c) .2443   (d) −1.3730
(e) 1.8600   (f) 9/4   (g) −1.2900   (h) 5.7200

9. Express each of the following as a single angle in degrees and minutes from 0′ to 59′.

(a) 15°27′ + 32°14′

(b) 18°41′ + 15°12′

(c) 13°32′ + 37°28′

(d) 142°5′ + 8°55′

(e) 29°43′ + 51°38′

(f) 61°19′ + 23°58′

(g) 180° − 15°13′

(h) 90° − 47°38′

(i) 360° − 147°23′

(j) 270° − 63°48′

(k) $\frac{1}{2}(18°47′ + 56°29′)$

(l) $\frac{1}{2}(56°28′ − 47°36′)$

10. If an arc 20 ft long subtends an angle of 2 radians at the center of a circle, find its radius.

11. If a wheel of radius 2 ft rolls 3 ft, how many radians has it turned? How many degrees has it turned?

12. In a circle of radius 14 inches, how long an arc does a central angle of 82° intersect?

13. How many degrees are there between the minute and hour hands of a clock at 4:00 o'clock? At 1:00? At 9:15? At 5:47?

14. Assuming that the earth's radius is 3960 miles, find the distance on the surface of the earth from Columbus, Ohio to the equator. The latitude of Columbus is 40°.

15. If a point on the circumference of a wheel whose diameter is 20 inches travels 3000 ft a minute, through how many radians does the wheel turn in one second?

16. For small angles, the intercepted arc and chord are approximately the same length. Assuming that the earth moves around the sun in a circle of 93,000,000 miles radius, find the sun's diameter if it subtends an angle of 32′ at the earth.

17. In the unit circle ($r = 1$), formula (2–7) becomes $s = \theta$. Explain the meaning of this extremely important formula. What would be the length of the arc of the unit circle intercepted by a central angle of 5 radians? 1 radian? θ radians?

2–3 Definitions of the circular functions. Consider an angle θ in standard position which has been generated by the portion of the rotating ray of length r (Fig. 2–4). Let (x,y) be the coordinates of P, the point on the terminal side of the angle, a distance r from the origin. We define the *sine, cosine,* and *tangent functions of θ* in terms of these coordinates and of r, the radius of the generated circle. Using the usual abbreviations, we have

$$\sin \theta = \frac{y}{r}, \qquad\qquad (2\text{--}8)$$

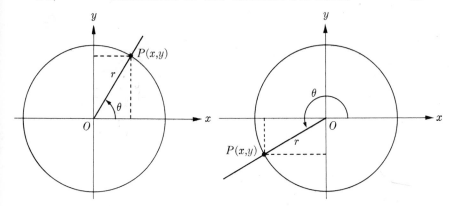

FIGURE 2–4

$$\cos \theta = \frac{x}{r}, \qquad (2\text{–}9)$$

and

$$\tan \theta = \frac{y}{x} \quad (x \neq 0). \qquad (2\text{–}10)$$

These functions are uniquely determined for any specific value of θ [except in (2–10) where, for certain values of θ, $\tan \theta$ is not defined because $x = 0$] and in no way depend upon the distance of P from the origin. To clarify this statement, consider the two concentric circles with r and r' as radii and $P(x,y)$ and $P'(x',y')$ lying on the terminal side of angle θ, as in Fig. 2–5. Since the right triangles formed with the lengths of the coordinates x, y, x', and y' as legs are similar, the corresponding ratios which define these functions are equal.

Notice the relationship between these functions. Since $\tan \theta = y/x = (y/r)/(x/r)$, we have

$$\tan \theta = \frac{\sin \theta}{\cos \theta}, \qquad (2\text{–}11)$$

which is defined for all values of θ except where $\cos \theta = 0$. In this case $\tan \theta$ is undefined (see Article 1–1).

From Article 1–4, we recall the signs of the coordinates of points in the different quadrants. In the same way, we determine in which quadrants the circular functions are positive or negative. Since

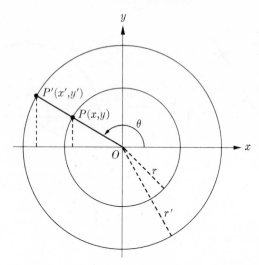

FIGURE 2–5

$r = \sqrt{x^2 + y^2} > 0$ in every quadrant, we have the following table, which the student should verify.

Quadrant	$\sin \theta = y/r$	$\cos \theta = x/r$	$\tan \theta = y/x$
I	+	+	+
II	+	−	−
III	−	−	+
IV	−	+	−

EXAMPLE 1. Let θ be an angle in standard position with its terminal side passing through $(-3,4)$. Find $\sin \theta$, $\cos \theta$, and $\tan \theta$.

Solution. Since $x = -3$ and $y = 4$, $r = \sqrt{(-3)^2 + 4^2} = \sqrt{9 + 16}$ $= \sqrt{25} = 5$. Thus, $\sin \theta = 4/5$, $\cos \theta = -3/5$, and $\tan \theta = -4/3$.

EXAMPLE 2. Find the value of $\cos \theta$ and $\tan \theta$ if $\sin \theta = -5/13$ and $\tan \theta > 0$.

Solution. Since $\sin \theta < 0$ and $\tan \theta > 0$, θ terminates in the third quadrant. Moreover, with $\sin \theta = -5/13$, we may assume that the terminal side of θ passes through $(-5,-12)$. (Why?) Therefore $\cos \theta = -12/13$, and $\tan \theta = 5/12$.

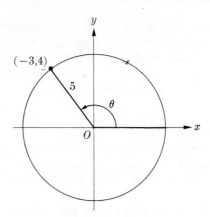

FIGURE 2–6

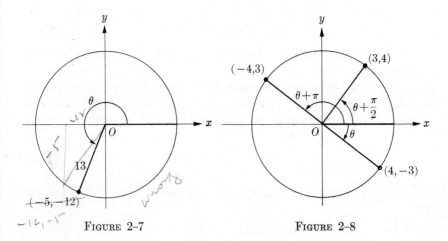

FIGURE 2–7   FIGURE 2–8

EXAMPLE 3.   Let θ be an angle in standard position with its terminal side passing through $(4,-3)$.   Find the sine, cosine, and tangent of $\theta + \pi/2$, and $\theta + \pi$.

Solution.   By similar right triangles the terminal side of $\theta + \pi/2$, in standard position, passes through $(3,4)$, while that of $\theta + \pi$ passes through $(-4,3)$.   Since $r = 5$ in all cases, we have

$$\begin{aligned}
\sin(\theta + \pi/2) &= 4/5, & \sin(\theta + \pi) &= 3/5, \\
\cos(\theta + \pi/2) &= 3/5, & \cos(\theta + \pi) &= -4/5, \\
\tan(\theta + \pi/2) &= 4/3, & \tan(\theta + \pi) &= -3/4.
\end{aligned}$$

If θ were increased or decreased by an integral multiple of 2π (or 360°) the terminal side of the new angle would coincide with the original terminal side, so that P would have the same coordinates. Therefore

$$\sin [\theta + k(2\pi)] = \sin \theta, \qquad (2\text{--}12)$$

and

$$\cos [\theta + k(2\pi)] = \cos \theta, \qquad (2\text{--}13)$$

where k is any integer. Hence, if we know the values of $\sin \theta$ and $\cos \theta$ in the range $0 \leqslant \theta \leqslant 2\pi$, we know their values for all θ. The sine and cosine functions are called *periodic functions* with a period of 2π.*

The tangent function differs from the sine and cosine functions. Since $\tan \theta = y/x = -y/-x$, and the point $P'(-x,-y)$ lies on the terminal side of the angle $\theta + \pi$,

$$\tan (\theta + k\pi) = \tan \theta, \qquad (2\text{--}14)$$

where k is any integer. The tangent function is periodic with a period of π.

There are three other circular functions of less importance than those already defined. The *cosecant, secant,* and *cotangent functions* are defined in terms of the coordinates of $P(x,y)$ as follows:

$$\csc \theta = \frac{r}{y} \quad (y \neq 0), \qquad (2\text{--}15)$$

$$\sec \theta = \frac{r}{x} \quad (x \neq 0), \qquad (2\text{--}16)$$

and

$$\cot \theta = \frac{x}{y} \quad (y \neq 0). \qquad (2\text{--}17)$$

It will be noticed immediately by using Eqs. (2–8,9,10) that

$$\sin \theta \csc \theta = 1, \qquad (2\text{--}18)$$

$$\cos \theta \sec \theta = 1, \qquad (2\text{--}19)$$

and

$$\tan \theta \cot \theta = 1. \qquad (2\text{--}20)$$

---

* In general, any function of θ is said to be *periodic* with period p, provided the function of $\theta + p$ is equal to the function of θ, and p is the smallest constant for which this is true. Note how $k = 1$ in Eq. (2–12) gives this smallest constant, 2π.

Because of this type of relationship, these three functions are called the *reciprocal functions*. If sin θ, cos θ, and tan θ are known, any of these other three functions can be found immediately. For this reason we shall not emphasize them.

PROBLEMS

Which of the following expressions are positive? Which are negative?

1. sin 164°	2. cos 158°	3. tan 195°
4. cos 327°	5. tan 227°	6. sin 264°
7. sin (−38°)	8. cot (−125°)	9. tan (−213°)
10. cos 2π/3	11. tan 5π/4	12. sin (−11π/6)
13. cot 9π/7	14. sec (−7π/8)	15. csc (−π/8)

Assuming that θ is in standard position, determine the quadrants in which θ may lie under the following conditions:

16. sin θ > 0	17. cos θ > 0
18. tan θ > 0 1 & 3	19. sin θ < 0
20. cos θ < 0	21. sec θ > 0
22. sin θ > 0 and cos θ > 0	23. cos θ > 0 and sin θ < 0
24. tan θ > 0 and sin θ < 0	25. sin θ > 0 and cos θ < 0
26. sin θ < 0 and cos θ < 0	

In each of the following the terminal side of the angle, in standard position, passes through the indicated point. Sketch and find the circular functions of each angle.

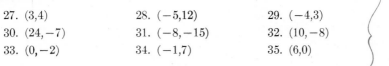

27. (3,4)	28. (−5,12)	29. (−4,3)
30. (24,−7)	31. (−8,−15)	32. (10,−8)
33. (0,−2)	34. (−1,7)	35. (6,0)

Find the values of sin θ, cos θ, and tan θ under the following conditions:

36. sin θ = 5/13, θ in the first quadrant.

37. cos θ = −4/5, θ in the third quadrant.

38. tan θ = −1/3, θ in the second quadrant.

39. sin θ = 2/3, θ not in the first quadrant.

40. cot θ = 4/3, θ not in the first quadrant.

41. cos θ = 5/6, θ not in the first quadrant.

42. tan θ = 1/2, and sin θ is positive.

43. sin θ = −3/5, and tan θ is positive.

44. $\cos \theta = -7/9$, and $\tan \theta$ is negative.

45. $\tan \theta = 2/3$.

46. $\sec \theta = -5/3$.

47. $\csc \theta = 12/7$.

In Problems 48 through 52, the terminal side of the angle θ, in standard position, passes through (8,15).

48. Sketch and find the circular functions of $\theta + \pi/2$.

49. Sketch and find the circular functions of $\theta + 180°$.

50. Sketch and find the circular functions of $\theta + 270°$.

51. Sketch and find the circular functions of $\theta - \pi$.

52. Sketch and find the circular functions of $\theta - 90°$.

53. For any angle θ in standard position with its terminal side intersecting the circle of radius r at P, show that P has coordinates $(r \cos \theta, \ r \sin \theta)$. This is a most important concept, and should be emphasized.

2–4 The unit circle. We have mentioned the *unit circle* with its center at the origin and a radius of one. Since the circular functions are independent of the radius of the circle, many general properties can be obtained through the use of this circle.

Consider the angle θ in standard position (Fig. 2–9), with its terminal side intersecting the unit circle at $P(x,y)$. Since $r = 1$, we have $\sin \theta = y$ and $\cos \theta = x$. In other words, P is the point with coordinates $(\cos \theta, \sin \theta)$. For certain angles the values of their

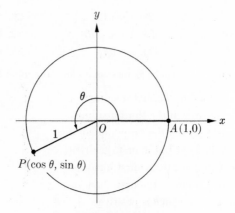

FIGURE 2–9

circular functions are immediately apparent. The terminal side of the angle $0° = 0$ radians coincides with the initial side, so that the coordinates of P are $(1,0)$. Hence,

$$\sin 0 = 0, \qquad \tan 0 = \frac{0}{1} = 0,$$

$$\cos 0 = 1, \qquad \sec 0 = \frac{1}{1} = 1,$$

while cot 0 and csc 0 (i.e., $1/0$) are undefined.

The angle $90° = \pi/2$ has its terminal side intersecting the unit circle at the point $(0,1)$. Using this fact, the values of circular functions of $90°$ are found. The functional values of the other *quadrantal angles* (any angle which is a multiple of $90°$) are also obtained by noting the coordinates of the point where the terminal side of the angle intersects the unit circle.

It is now clear how the values of these functions change as θ increases from 0 to 2π. Verify the following table:

Quadrant	θ varies from	Value of $\sin \theta$ varies from	Value of $\cos \theta$ varies from
I	0 to 90° (0 to $\pi/2$)	0 to 1	1 to 0
II	90° to 180° ($\pi/2$ to π)	1 to 0	0 to -1
III	180° to 270° (π to $3\pi/2$)	0 to -1	-1 to 0
IV	270° to 360° ($3\pi/2$ to 2π)	-1 to 0	0 to 1

The fact that the values of the sine and cosine function are never larger than one is apparent from the table. That this must be so is clear, since they are the coordinates of some point on the unit circle. The tangent, however, can have any positive or negative real number for its value.

As the point $P(\cos \theta, \sin \theta)$ is thought of as moving around the unit circle, we have observed the changes in both $\sin \theta$ and $\cos \theta$. If we wish to consider the behavior of $\sin \theta$ alone, a study of the graph of $y = \sin \theta$ is most convenient, with values of θ plotted on the horizontal axis, and values of y on the vertical axis. Such a graph may be obtained directly from the unit circle.

Consider a rectangular coordinate system with intervals $\pi/2$ in length laid off along the θ-axis, as in Fig. 2–10. A unit circle is drawn

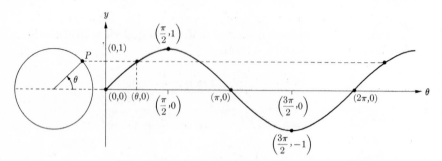

FIGURE 2–10

with its center on the θ-axis. To obtain the graph of $y = \sin \theta$, the ordinate of P is carried over to the point whose abscissa is θ. As many points as may be desired on the graph are obtained by repeated bisection of the four quadrants. By drawing a smooth curve through the points located in this way, we have a graph of $y = \sin \theta$.* The curve continues indefinitely to the right and left, but need only be drawn from 0 to 2π. (Why?)

With the use of radian measure and the unit circle, the value of θ corresponds exactly to the length of its subtended arc. Thus in Fig. 2–10, the length of the arc $\overset{\frown}{AP}$ is equal to the distance from 0 to θ on the θ-axis. Notice how clearly the following properties are shown by the graph of $y = \sin \theta$.

1.   This function is periodic with period 2π. [Recall Eq. (2–12).]

2.   In the first quadrant this function is an *increasing function*.†
In what other quadrant is this the case?

3.   The values of $\sin \theta$ are positive for θ, in the first and second quadrants, and negative in the third and fourth quadrants.

4.   The values of $\sin \theta$ lie between -1 and $+1$.

5.   The zeros of $\sin \theta$ are at multiples of π,

$$\sin k\pi = 0, \qquad k = 0, \pm 1, \pm 2, \cdots.$$

In Fig. 2–11, the graph of $y = \cos \theta$ is shown, which may be constructed by a procedure similar to the one just described. Using

---

* Such a graph may also be plotted using points, whose coordinates are obtained from Table I in this book. A further discussion of graphing appears in Chapter 5.

† If $\theta_1 > \theta_2$, then $\sin \theta_1 > \sin \theta_2$.

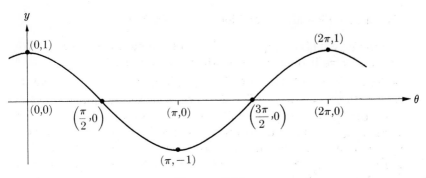

FIGURE 2–11

this figure, it is helpful to make a list of some of the properties of $y = \cos \theta$.

We have already noticed certain relations between the various functions such as (2–11,18,19,20). Others can also be derived. Since $\cot \theta = 1/\tan \theta$ [see (2–20)], and $\tan \theta = \sin \theta/\cos \theta$ [see (2–11)],

$$\cot \theta = \frac{\cos \theta}{\sin \theta}. \tag{2–21}$$

More important, however, are the following results. Since the co-ordinates of any point on the unit circle are $(\cos \theta, \sin \theta)$, and these coordinates must satisfy the equation of the unit circle, $x^2 + y^2 = 1$, we have

$$\sin^2 \theta + \cos^2 \theta = 1 \tag{2–22}$$

for any value of θ, where $\sin^2 \theta$ is the usual notation for $(\sin \theta)^2$, and so on. By dividing each term of (2–22) by $\cos^2 \theta$, we get

$$\frac{\sin^2 \theta}{\cos^2 \theta} + 1 = \frac{1}{\cos^2 \theta},$$

or

$$\tan^2 \theta + 1 = \sec^2 \theta. \tag{2–23}$$

By dividing each term of (2–22) by $\sin^2 \theta$, we get

$$1 + \frac{\cos^2 \theta}{\sin^2 \theta} = \frac{1}{\sin^2 \theta},$$

or

$$1 + \cot^2 \theta = \csc^2 \theta. \tag{2–24}$$

EXAMPLE. Find all six functions of θ if $\cos \theta = 3/5$.

Solution. This example is similar to Example 2, Article 2–3. We can now solve it by a second method. Using (2–19), we have sec θ = 5/3. From (2–22) $\sin \theta = \pm \sqrt{1 - \cos^2\theta} = \pm \sqrt{1 - 9/25} = \pm \sqrt{16/25} = \pm 4/5$. The sign depends on the quadrant of θ. Since $\cos \theta > 0$, we know θ is in the first or fourth quadrant. If it were in the first, the plus sign would appear before the 4/5; if it were in the fourth, the minus sign would be chosen. From (2–11), $\tan \theta = \sin \theta / \cos \theta = \pm (4/5)/(3/5) = \pm 4/3$. Using (2–18), cot θ = $\pm 3/4$, and (2–15) gives us csc $\theta = \pm 5/4$.

PROBLEMS

1. What are the values of the six circular functions of θ when $\theta = \pi$? Recall that the coordinates of P in this case are $(-1,0)$.

2. What are the values of the six circular functions of $\theta = 270°$?

3. What are the values of the six circular functions of 2π? How do these values compare with those for $\theta = 0$?

4. What are the values of the six circular functions of $-\pi/2$?

5. What are the values of the six circular functions of the following angles:

(a) 3π	(b) $7\pi/2$	(c) $9\pi/2$
(d) 16π	(e) 15π	(f) 100π
(g) $450°$	(h) $720°$	(i) $900°$

6. What are the values of the six circular functions of the following angles:

(a) -5π	(b) $-\pi/2$	(c) $-3\pi/2$
(d) -6π	(e) $-11\pi/2$	(f) -40π
(g) $-180°$	(h) $-630°$	(i) $-450°$

7. Verify the table in this article for the variation of $\sin \theta$ and $\cos \theta$.

8. Make a similar table for the other four functions.

9–20. Do Problems 36 through 47 of Article 2–3 by the method outlined in the example of this article.

21. Show that $\sin (k\pi) = 0$ and $\cos (k\pi) = (-1)^k$ for any integer k (positive, negative, or zero).

22. Construct a graph of $y = \cos \theta$, as in Fig. 2–11, indicating the procedure used. From the graph list properties for $y = \cos \theta$, similar to those listed for $y = \sin \theta$.

23. In the same rectangular coordinate system sketch both the curve $y = \sin\theta$ and $y = \cos\theta$, one curve superimposed on the other. Although the following facts will be proved in Chapter 3, could they be deduced from the figure?

(a) $\sin(\pi/2 + \theta) = \sin(\pi/2 - \theta)$,   (d) $\cos(-\theta) = \cos\theta$,

(b) $\sin(-\theta) = -\sin\theta$,   (e) $\cos\theta = \sin(\pi/2 - \theta)$,

(c) $\cos(\pi/2 - \theta) = -\cos(\pi/2 + \theta)$,   (f) $\sin\theta = \cos(\pi/2 - \theta)$.

24. Obtain an expression in terms of θ for the length of any chord (in a unit circle) whose corresponding arc is subtended by the central angle θ. *Hint.* In Fig. 2–9, the coordinates of A are $(1,0)$ and of P are $(\cos\theta, \sin\theta)$. Using the distance formula (1–5),

$$AP = \sqrt{(1 - \cos\theta)^2 + \sin^2\theta}$$

$$= \sqrt{1 - 2\cos\theta + \cos^2\theta + \sin^2\theta},$$

or

$$\text{Length of Chord} = \sqrt{2 - 2\cos\theta}. \qquad (2\text{--}25)$$

25. Find the length of the chord in a unit circle, if the subtending angle is (a) $\pi/2$, (b) π.

26. In Fig. 2–12, the terminal side of angle θ intersects the unit circle at P. Draw the tangent to the circle at A and extend the terminal side from the origin O through P. The point at which these lines intersect can be called R. Labeling the point $(0,1)$ on the circle B, draw the tangent to the circle through this point. This tangent line will intersect the line from O through P and the tangent line to the circle at A. Call these points S and T respectively. (a) Verify for this figure that $\tan\theta$ is equal in magnitude to the length of the

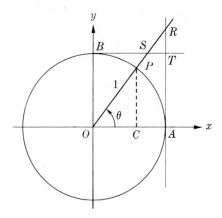

FIGURE 2–12

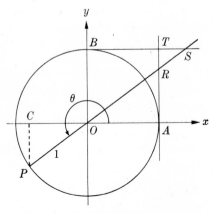

FIGURE 2–13

line segment AR.   Draw a line from P perpendicular to the x-axis.   Calling the foot of this perpendicular C, triangle OPC is similar to ORA.   Use the ratio of similar sides of these triangles to obtain the result.   (b) Verify that $\cot \theta$ is equal in magnitude to the length of the line segment BS.

27. Figure 2–13 has been drawn in the same manner as Fig. 2–12 except that P is in the third quadrant.   In a similar manner, construct two other figures, one where θ is in the second quadrant and one where θ is in the fourth quadrant.

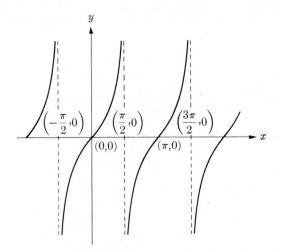

FIGURE 2–14

28. Employing the figures from Problem 27, Fig. 2–12 and Fig. 2–13, and the results of Problem 26, verify that the following definitions are equivalent to the original definitions: (a) $\tan \theta$ is the y-coordinate of the point R, (b) $\cot \theta$ is the x-coordinate of the point S.

29. By using the unit circle and the definition for $\tan \theta$ given in Problem 28, construct a graph of $y = \tan \theta$ (see Fig. 2–14).

30. From the graph of $y = \tan \theta$ given in Fig. 2–14, list properties for this function similar to those listed for $y = \sin \theta$.

2–5 Values of special angle functions. In addition to the quadrantal angles, the circular functions of certain other angles can be found exactly. Consider the angle $\pi/6 = 30°$, located in standard position with the unit circle in Fig. 2–15. In plane geometry, it is shown that in a right triangle with an angle of 30°, the hypotenuse is twice as long as the side opposite this angle. Since the point P' lies on the unit circle and has $1/2$ for its y-coordinate, substituting in $x^2 + y^2 = 1$, the equation of the circle, we have $x^2 + (1/2)^2 = 1$ or $x^2 = 3/4$. Thus, in the first quadrant, $x = \sqrt{3}/2$, and

$$\sin 30° = 1/2, \qquad \cot 30° = \sqrt{3},$$
$$\cos 30° = \sqrt{3}/2, \qquad \sec 30° = 2/\sqrt{3},$$
$$\tan 30° = 1/\sqrt{3}, \qquad \csc 30° = 2.$$

By properly placing the 30°–60° triangle in the unit circle, the coordinates of a point on the terminal side of any nonquadrantal angle

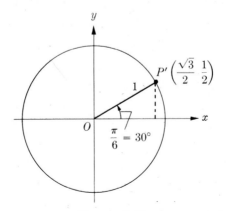

FIGURE 2–15

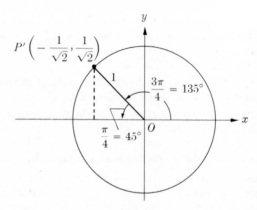

FIGURE 2–16

of size $k \cdot 30°$, with k an integer, can be found. From these the values of the circular functions of any such angle result.

Again consider $\theta = 3\pi/4 = 135°$. Since $135° = 90° + 45°$ in Fig. 2–16, the right triangle, with OP' as hypotenuse and also as the terminal side of the angle $135°$, is isosceles. Since P' lies on the unit circle and has x- and y-coordinates equal in size, with $y = -x$, on substituting, we have $x^2 + x^2 = 2x^2 = 1$, or $x = -1/\sqrt{2}$. Hence,

$$\sin 135° = 1/\sqrt{2}, \qquad \cot 135° = -1,$$

$$\cos 135° = -1/\sqrt{2}, \qquad \sec 135° = -\sqrt{2},$$

$$\tan 135° = -1, \qquad \csc 135° = \sqrt{2}.$$

The values of the circular functions of any other odd multiple of $45°$ can be obtained by similar methods.

PROBLEMS

Draw a figure showing each angle in the unit circle, and verify the following by finding the exact values.

1. (a) $\sin \pi/3 = \cos \pi/6$ (b) $\sin 30° = \cos 60°$
2. (a) $\sin \pi/6 = \sin 5\pi/6$ (b) $\cos 150° = -\cos 30°$
3. (a) $\tan 45° = \tan 225°$ (b) $\cot 135° = \cot 315°$
4. (a) $\sec 11\pi/6 = \sec \pi/6$ (b) $\csc 2\pi/3 = -\csc 4\pi/3$
5. (a) $\sin 120° = \sin (-240°)$ (b) $\cos 7\pi/6 = \cos (-5\pi/6)$

6. (a) $\sin 60° = 2 \sin 30° \cos 30°$

  (b) $\sin \pi/2 = 2 \sin \pi/4 \cos \pi/4$

7. (a) $\sin \pi/6 = \sqrt{\dfrac{1 - \cos \pi/3}{2}}$ (b) $\cos \pi/6 = \sqrt{\dfrac{1 + \cos \pi/3}{2}}$

8. $\tan 30° = \dfrac{1 - \cos 60°}{\sin 60°} = \dfrac{\sin 60°}{1 + \cos 60°}$

9. $\cos 60° = \cos^2 30° - \sin^2 30° = 2 \cos^2 30° - 1$

Find the exact numerical values of the following:

10. (a) $\sin^2 \pi/6 + \cos^2 \pi/6$ (b) $\sin^2 0 + \cos^2 0$

11. (a) $\sec^2 \pi/3 - \tan^2 \pi/3$ (b) $\sec^2 5\pi/4 - \tan^2 5\pi/4$

12. (a) $\csc^2 315° - \cot^2 315°$ (b) $\csc^2 135° - \cot^2 135°$

13. $\sin 2\pi/3 + \cos 7\pi/6 + \tan 5\pi/3$

14. $\tan 5\pi/4 + \cot 7\pi/4 - \sec 5\pi/6$

15. $\csc 150° - \cos 240° + \tan 120°$

16. $\sin 120° \cos 150° + \cos 120° \sin 150°$

17. $\cos 3\pi/4 \cos \pi/4 - \sin 3\pi/4 \sin \pi/4$

18. $\sin 330° \cos 120° \tan 135°$

19. $(\cos 11\pi/6 + \sin \pi/3)(\tan \pi/6 + \cot 4\pi/3)$

20. $(\tan 5\pi/4 + \sin 3\pi/2) \cos 5\pi/6$

Find all the angles between 0° and 360° that satisfy each of the following equations, and express your answers in degrees and in radians:

21. $\sin \theta = 1/2$ 22. $\cos \theta = -1/2$

23. $\tan \theta = 1/\sqrt{3}$ 24. $\sin \theta = -\sqrt{3}/2$

25. $\tan \theta = -1$ 26. $\cos \theta = -\sqrt{2}/2$

27. $\sin \theta = \sqrt{2}/2$ 28. $\sec \theta = 2$

29. $\cot \theta = -\sqrt{3}$ 30. $\csc \theta = 2/\sqrt{3}$

31. By drawing a figure for each of the following angles in the unit circle, make a table giving the angle in both degrees and radians, and the six circular functions of each: 0°, 30°, 45°, 60°, 90°, 120°, 135°, 150°, 180°, 210°, 225°, 240°, 270°, 300°, 315°, 330°, 360°.

32. Using formula (2–25) find the length of the chord in a unit circle if the subtending angle is (a) $\pi/6$, (b) $\pi/3$, (c) $2\pi/3$.

*2–6 Exact values of the functions for $\theta = \pi/5$. There is one other special value of an angle which is of interest. Although a slightly more complicated construction is required for $36° = \pi/5$, we

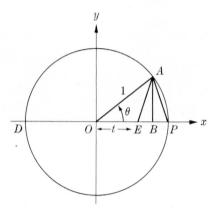

FIGURE 2–17

are able to find exact values for the circular functions of this angle, and thus have exact values for the functions of π, $\pi/2$, $\pi/3$, $\pi/4$, $\pi/5$, and $\pi/6$. Consider the unit circle with center O and radius OP (see Fig. 2–17). Locate the point E so that

$$\frac{\text{Length } OP}{\text{Length } OE} = \frac{\text{Length } OE^*}{\text{Length } EP} .$$

By letting t denote the length of OE, we have the relationship

$$\frac{1}{t} = \frac{t}{1 - t} . \qquad (2\text{–}26)\dagger$$

---

* This location is possible with the use of ruler and compass, and is essentially the same as that used for constructing a regular pentagon.

† The ratio defined by Eq. (2–26) has been considered since the time of the Greek mathematicians, and is called the *golden section*. Much has been written on this subject which would be of interest to the student as additional reading. For example:

1. H. V. Baravalle, The Geometry of the Pentagon and the Golden Section, *Mathematics Teacher*, Jan. 1948.

2. W. W. Rouse Ball, *Mathematical Recreations and Essays*, rev. by H. S. M. Coxeter, 11th Ed. London: Macmillan and Company, Limited, 1940.

3. R. Courant and H. Robbins, *What is Mathematics?* New York: Oxford University Press, 1941.

4. Jay Hambridge, *The Elements of Dynamic Symmetry*. New York: Brentano's, 1926.

Solving this quadratic equation for the positive value of t, we find $t = (\sqrt{5} - 1)/2$.

Locate A so that the length of the chord AP is equal to t. Therefore the triangles OPA and AEP are similar, and thus triangle AEP is isosceles, so that the length of $AE = t$, and triangle OEA is also isosceles. From this it follows directly that $\angle OPA$ is twice $\angle AOP$ (see Problems 3, 4, and 5). Since $\angle OPA$ is measured by $\frac{1}{2}\stackrel{\frown}{AD}$,* $\angle AOP$ is measured by $\frac{1}{4}\stackrel{\frown}{AD}$. Also $\angle AOP$ is measured by $\stackrel{\frown}{AP}$. Thus $\stackrel{\frown}{AD} = 4\stackrel{\frown}{AP}$. But $\stackrel{\frown}{AD} + \stackrel{\frown}{AP} = \pi$. As a direct result, $\stackrel{\frown}{AP} = \pi/5$ and $\theta = \pi/5 = 36°$.

By considering AB perpendicular to OP at B, we easily find the exact lengths of OB and AB, that is, the cosine and sine of $\pi/5$. The length of $EP = 1 - t = 1 - \dfrac{\sqrt{5} - 1}{2} = \dfrac{3 - \sqrt{5}}{2}$; thus the length of EB is $\dfrac{3 - \sqrt{5}}{4}$. Therefore the length of $OB = \dfrac{\sqrt{5} - 1}{2}$ $+ \dfrac{3 - \sqrt{5}}{4} = \dfrac{\sqrt{5} + 1}{4}$. Also, in the right triangle OAB, (length of $AB)^2 = 1 - \left(\dfrac{\sqrt{5} + 1}{4}\right)^2 = \dfrac{5 - \sqrt{5}}{8}$. Thus

$$\sin \frac{\pi}{5} = \sqrt{\frac{5 - \sqrt{5}}{8}}, \qquad \cos \frac{\pi}{5} = \frac{\sqrt{5} + 1}{4} . \qquad (2\text{–}27)$$

Should the numerical values of the other functions be desired, they can now be found.

PROBLEMS

Referring to Fig. 2–17, prove the following in detail:

1. Triangle AEP is isosceles.
2. Triangle OEA is isosceles.
3. Angles AOP, OAE, and EAP are equal.
4. $\angle OAP = \angle OPA$.

---

* Use is made of the theorem in plane geometry which states: an angle inscribed in a circle is measured by one-half the intercepted arc.

5. $\angle APO$ = twice $\angle AOP$.

6. Using formula (2–25), find the length of the chord in a unit circle which is subtended by the angle $\pi/5$.   How does this value compare with the value of t?

CHAPTER 3

FUNCTIONS INVOLVING MORE THAN ONE ANGLE

This chapter deals with two additional general types of circular function relations, which differ from those studied thus far in that they contain functions of more than one angle. Not only do we frequently encounter the problem of expressing a circular function of θ plus some multiple of $\pi/2$ as a function of θ only, but often we wish to consider circular functions of two angles in general. Such functions, we shall see, can be expressed in terms of functions of each angle separately. More specifically, we know that $\sin(\pi/4 + \pi/3)$ is not equal to $\sin \pi/4 + \sin \pi/3$, since the latter is equal to $1/\sqrt{2} + \sqrt{3}/2$ (a value greater than one), an impossible value for the sine function. However, $\sin(\pi/4 + \pi/3)$ can be expressed in terms of functions of $\pi/4$ and $\pi/3$, and its value readily obtained. We find it convenient to develop first a formula for $\cos(\alpha - \beta)$.

3-1 Proof of the formula for $\cos(\alpha - \beta)$. We wish to prove one of the most basic formulas of Trigonometry,

$$\cos(\alpha - \beta) = \cos\alpha\cos\beta + \sin\alpha\sin\beta. \tag{3-1}$$

As in Fig. 3-1, let α and β be any two angles in standard position in the unit circle. Denote by P_α and P_β the points where the terminal

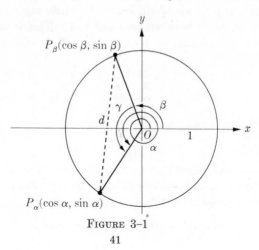

$$P_\beta(\cos\beta, \sin\beta)$$

$$P_\alpha(\cos\alpha, \sin\alpha)$$

FIGURE 3-1

41

sides of the angles intersect the unit circle. Since the coordinates of P_α are $(\cos \alpha, \sin \alpha)$ and of P_β are $(\cos \beta, \sin \beta)$, the distance d between these two points [Eq. (1–5)] is given by

$$d = \sqrt{(\cos \alpha - \cos \beta)^2 + (\sin \alpha - \sin \beta)^2}$$
$$= \sqrt{\cos^2 \alpha - 2 \cos \alpha \cos \beta + \cos^2 \beta + \sin^2 \alpha - 2 \sin \alpha \sin \beta + \sin^2 \beta}$$
$$= \sqrt{2 - 2 (\cos \alpha \cos \beta + \sin \alpha \sin \beta)}.$$

By recalling (2–25), the expression for the length of any chord whose subtending angle is θ in the unit circle, we have another expression for d. Since d represents the length of the chord whose subtending angle is γ, where $\gamma = (\alpha - \beta) \pm$ some integral multiple of 360°,

$$d = \sqrt{2 - 2 \cos \gamma}$$
$$= \sqrt{2 - 2 \cos (\alpha - \beta)}.$$

Upon equating these two expressions for d and simplifying, we see that

$$\cos (\alpha - \beta) = \cos \alpha \cos \beta + \sin \alpha \sin \beta, \qquad (3\text{–}1)$$

which was to be proved. It should be pointed out, and emphasized, that this formula expresses the cosine of $\alpha - \beta$ in terms of the functions of α and β themselves, and holds for any value of α or β. It is in this respect that the formula becomes important.

3–2 Special reduction formulas. As is probably somewhat evident by this time, any circular function of any angle can be expressed as a function of an angle between zero and $\pi/4$. This is shown by using certain reduction formulas derived from (3–1) with special values for α or β.

If we replace α by 90° in (3–1), we obtain

$$\cos (90° - \beta) = \cos 90° \cos \beta + \sin 90° \sin \beta.$$

Since $\cos 90° = 0$ and $\sin 90° = 1$, we have

$$\cos (90° - \beta) = \sin \beta. \qquad (3\text{–}2)$$

It should be emphasized that these relations hold for all angles α or β, and the reader should observe this as the formulas are derived. If in (3–2) we replace β by 90° − β, the relation

$$\cos [90° - (90° - \beta)] = \sin (90° - \beta)$$

holds for all β.   Simplifying, this becomes

$$\sin (90° - \beta) = \cos \beta. \tag{3-3}$$

From (3–2) and (3–3), we immediately see that

$$\tan (90° - \beta) = \cot \beta, \tag{3-4}$$

and

$$\cot (90° - \beta) = \tan \beta. \tag{3-5}$$

Although true for all values, these four results are especially useful for acute angles when computation is involved.   For example, $\sin 56° = \cos 34°$, $\tan 81° = \cot 9°$, or $\cos 72° = \sin 18°$.

We have noticed that circular functions have names which can be paired.   In each pair, one function is the *cofunction* of the other.   The sine is the cofunction of the cosine, and the cosine is the cofunction of the sine, and so on.   With this concept of cofunction, the four relations above can be stated: The cofunction of any angle equals the function of the *complementary* angle.

The relationship between the functions of any angle and its negative are most useful, and also follow from (3–1).   Letting $\alpha = 0°$,

$$\cos (0° - \beta) = \cos 0° \cos \beta + \sin 0° \sin \beta.$$

Since $\cos 0° = 1$ and $\sin 0° = 0$,

$$\cos (-\beta) = \cos \beta. \tag{3-6}$$

Also, if we replace β by $-\beta$ in (3–2),

$$\cos (90° + \beta) = \sin (-\beta).$$

Since $90° + \beta = \beta - (-90°)$,

$$\sin (-\beta) = \cos [\beta - (-90°)]$$
$$= \cos \beta \cos (-90°) + \sin \beta \sin (-90°)$$
$$= (\cos \beta)(0) + (\sin \beta)(-1),$$

or

$$\sin (-\beta) = -\sin \beta. \tag{3-7}$$

It follows directly that

$$\tan (-\beta) = -\tan \beta. \tag{3-8}$$

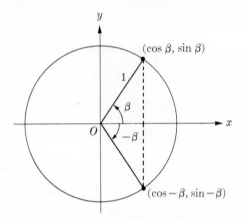

FIGURE 3–2

For example, $\sin(-15°) = -\sin 15°$, and $\tan(-176°) = -\tan 176°$, but $\cos(-279°) = \cos 279°$. Notice the significance of (3–6) and (3–7) in Fig. 3–2.

3–3 General addition formulas. We shall now derive the general formulas for the sine, cosine, and tangent of the sum or difference of two angles. Since

$$\cos(\alpha + \beta) = \cos[\alpha - (-\beta)]$$
$$= \cos\alpha\cos(-\beta) + \sin\alpha\sin(-\beta),$$

we have

$$\cos(\alpha + \beta) = \cos\alpha\cos\beta - \sin\alpha\sin\beta. \qquad (3\text{–}9)$$

Also,

$$\sin(\alpha + \beta) = \cos[90° - (\alpha + \beta)]$$
$$= \cos[(90° - \alpha) - \beta]$$
$$= \cos(90° - \alpha)\cos\beta + \sin(90° - \alpha)\sin\beta$$

and we have

$$\sin(\alpha + \beta) = \sin\alpha\cos\beta + \cos\alpha\sin\beta. \qquad (3\text{–}10)$$

Replacing β by $-\beta$ in (3–9), we immediately find

$$\sin(\alpha - \beta) = \sin\alpha\cos\beta - \cos\alpha\sin\beta. \qquad (3\text{–}11)$$

The tangent formulas,

$$\tan (\alpha + \beta) = \frac{\tan \alpha + \tan \beta}{1 - \tan \alpha \tan \beta} \qquad (3\text{-}12)$$

and

$$\tan (\alpha - \beta) = \frac{\tan \alpha - \tan \beta}{1 + \tan \alpha \tan \beta}, \qquad (3\text{-}13)$$

result from the fact that $\tan \theta = \sin \theta / \cos \theta$.

By using (3–9) and (3–10),

$$\tan (\alpha + \beta) = \frac{\sin (\alpha + \beta)}{\cos (\alpha + \beta)}$$

$$= \frac{\sin \alpha \cos \beta + \cos \alpha \sin \beta}{\cos \alpha \cos \beta - \sin \alpha \sin \beta}$$

$$= \frac{\dfrac{\sin \alpha \cos \beta}{\cos \alpha \cos \beta} + \dfrac{\cos \alpha \sin \beta}{\cos \alpha \cos \beta}}{\dfrac{\cos \alpha \cos \beta}{\cos \alpha \cos \beta} - \dfrac{\sin \alpha \sin \beta}{\cos \alpha \cos \beta}}$$

$$= \frac{\tan \alpha + \tan \beta}{1 - \tan \alpha \tan \beta}.$$

Formula (3–13) may be derived in a similar way, or by using (3–8).

EXAMPLE 1.   Compute $\sin 7\pi/12$ from the functions of $\pi/3$ and $\pi/4$.

Solution. $\sin 7\pi/12 = \sin (\pi/3 + \pi/4)$
$$= \sin \pi/3 \cos \pi/4 + \cos \pi/3 \sin \pi/4$$
$$= \sqrt{3}/2 \cdot \sqrt{2}/2 + 1/2 \cdot \sqrt{2}/2$$
$$= \sqrt{6}/4 + \sqrt{2}/4 = (\sqrt{6} + \sqrt{2})/4.$$

EXAMPLE 2.   Compute $\cos 15°$.

Solution. $\cos 15° = \cos (60° - 45°)$
$$= \cos 60° \cos 45° + \sin 60° \sin 45°$$
$$= 1/2 \cdot \sqrt{2}/2 + \sqrt{3}/2 \cdot \sqrt{2}/2$$
$$= \sqrt{2}/4 + \sqrt{6}/4 = (\sqrt{2} + \sqrt{6})/4.$$

EXAMPLE 3. Given $\sin \alpha = 12/13$, with α in the first quadrant, and $\cos \beta = 3/5$, with β in the first quadrant. Find in what quadrant $\alpha + \beta$ lies.

Solution. Since α and β are both in the first quadrant, $\alpha + \beta$ is either in the first or second quadrant. Since the cosine is positive in the first and negative in the second, it will suffice to find $\cos (\alpha + \beta)$. We are able to find $\cos \alpha$ and $\sin \beta$ as in Chapter 2: $\cos \alpha = 5/13$, and $\sin \beta = 4/5$. Thus

$$\cos (\alpha + \beta) = \cos \alpha \cos \beta - \sin \alpha \sin \beta$$
$$= 5/13 \cdot 3/5 - 12/13 \cdot 4/5$$
$$= 15/65 - 48/65 = -33/65.$$

Since $\cos (\alpha + \beta)$ is negative, it follows that $\alpha + \beta$ is in the second quadrant.

EXAMPLE 4. Show that $\sin (270° - \theta) = -\cos \theta$.

Solution. In (3–11) let $\alpha = 270°$ and $\beta = \theta$. Therefore,

$$\sin (270° - \theta) = \sin 270° \cos \theta - \cos 270° \sin \theta$$
$$= (-1) \cos \theta - (0) \sin \theta$$
$$= -\cos \theta.$$

EXAMPLE 5. Express $3 \sin \theta + 4 \cos \theta$ in the form $k \sin (\theta + \theta_1)$, where θ_1 is in the first quadrant.

Solution. By multiplying and dividing the expression by $\sqrt{3^2 + 4^2} = 5$, we have

$$5(\tfrac{3}{5} \sin \theta + \tfrac{4}{5} \cos \theta) = 5(\sin \theta \cdot \tfrac{3}{5} + \cos \theta \cdot \tfrac{4}{5}).$$

Letting $\cos \theta_1 = 3/5$, we find that $\sin \theta_1 = 4/5$; thus the above expression becomes

$$5(\sin \theta \cos \theta_1 + \cos \theta \sin \theta_1) = 5 \sin (\theta + \theta_1),$$

where θ_1 has its sine equal to $4/5$ and its cosine equal to $3/5$.

PROBLEMS

1. Find the exact value of the sine, cosine, and tangent of $5\pi/12 = 75°$ by setting $\alpha = 45°$ and $\beta = 30°$ in the appropriate one of the formulas previously derived.

2. Find the exact value of sin 15° and tan 15° by taking 15° = 60° − 45°.

3. Find the exact value of cos $7\pi/12$ and tan $7\pi/12$, as done in Example 1.

4. Find the exact values of the sine, cosine, and tangent of $11\pi/12 = 165°$ by setting $\alpha = 3\pi/4$ and $\beta = \pi/6$.

It is interesting to note that with the results of Problems 1–4, and previously known results, the exact values of the circular functions of any integral multiple of $\pi/12$ have been or can be readily found.

5. If sin $\alpha = 4/5$, and sin $\beta = 12/13$, and both α and β are in the first quadrant, find

(a) sin $(\alpha + \beta)$ (b) cos $(\alpha + \beta)$ (c) tan $(\alpha + \beta)$
(d) sin $(\alpha - \beta)$ (e) cos $(\alpha - \beta)$ (f) tan $(\alpha - \beta)$

6. If cos $\alpha = -24/25$, tan $\beta = 9/40$, α is in the second quadrant, and β is in the third quadrant, find

(a) sin $(\alpha + \beta)$ (b) cos $(\alpha + \beta)$ (c) tan $(\alpha + \beta)$
(d) sin $(\alpha - \beta)$ (e) cos $(\alpha - \beta)$ (f) tan $(\alpha - \beta)$

7. (a) In what quadrant is $\alpha + \beta$ in Problem 5?   (b) In what quadrant is $\alpha - \beta$ in Problem 6?

Find sin $(\alpha + \beta)$ and cos $(\alpha + \beta)$, given that:

8. tan $\alpha = 3/4$, sec $\beta = 13/5$, and neither α nor β is in the first quadrant.

9. tan $\alpha = -15/8$, sin $\beta = -7/25$, and neither α nor β is in the fourth quadrant.

Express each of the following in terms of functions of θ only:

10. cos $(\pi/4 + \theta)$ 11. tan $(\theta + \pi/6)$
12. sec $(\theta - 45°)$ 13. cot $(\pi/4 + \theta)$
14. sin $(\theta + 60°)$ 15. csc $(\theta - 30°)$
16. cos $(\pi/6 - \theta)$ 17. sin $(\theta - 45°)$

Show that the following statements are true.

18. tan $(\theta + \pi/4) - $ tan $(\theta - 3\pi/4) = 0$
19. sin $(\theta - \pi/6) + $ cos $(\theta - \pi/3) = 3$ sin θ
20. cot $(\alpha + \beta) = \dfrac{\cot \alpha \cot \beta - 1}{\cot \alpha + \cot \beta}$
21. tan $(\theta + \pi/4) = (1 + $ tan $\theta)/(1 - $ tan $\theta)$
22. sin $(\alpha + \beta)$ cos α cos $\beta = $ tan $\alpha + $ tan β
23. (a) sin $(\alpha + \beta) + $ sin $(\alpha - \beta) = 2$ sin α cos β
    (b) sin $(\alpha + \beta) - $ sin $(\alpha - \beta) = 2$ cos α sin β

24. (a) $\cos (\alpha + \beta) + \cos (\alpha - \beta) = 2 \cos \alpha \cos \beta$

    (b) $\cos (\alpha + \beta) - \cos (\alpha - \beta) = -2 \sin \alpha \sin \beta$

25. By letting $\alpha + \beta = x$, and $\alpha - \beta = y$, and dividing the respective members of Problems 23(a) and (b), prove

$$\frac{\sin x - \sin y}{\sin x + \sin y} = \frac{\tan \frac{1}{2}(x - y)}{\tan \frac{1}{2}(x + y)} .$$

26. (a) $\sin (\alpha + \beta) \sin (\alpha - \beta) = \sin^2 \alpha - \sin^2 \beta$

    (b) $\cos (\alpha + \beta) \cos (\alpha - \beta) = \cos^2 \alpha - \sin^2 \beta$

27. $\cos (\alpha + \beta) \cos \beta + \sin (\alpha + \beta) \sin \beta = \cos \alpha$

28. $\sin (\alpha - \beta) \cos \beta + \cos (\alpha - \beta) \sin \beta = \sin \alpha$

29. (a) $\cos \theta = \cos (\theta/2 + \theta/2) = \cos^2 (\theta/2) - \sin^2 (\theta/2) = 1 - 2 \sin^2 (\theta/2)$

    (b) $\cos \theta = 2 \cos^2 (\theta/2) - 1$

30. $\sin \theta = 2 \sin \dfrac{\theta}{2} \cos \dfrac{\theta}{2}$

31. $\sin \dfrac{\theta}{2} = \pm \sqrt{\dfrac{1 - \cos \theta}{2}}$.   *Hint:* Use Problem 29(a).

32. $\cos \dfrac{\theta}{2} = \pm \sqrt{\dfrac{1 + \cos \theta}{2}}$.   *Hint:* Use Problem 29(b).

Express the following in the form $k \sin (\theta + \theta_1)$, where θ_1 is between $\pi/2$ and $\pi/2$.

33. $5 \sin \theta + 12 \cos \theta$ 34. $15 \sin \theta + 8 \cos \theta$

35. $4 \sin \theta - 3 \cos \theta$ 36. $24 \sin \theta + 7 \cos \theta$

37. $\sin \theta + \cos \theta$ 38. $2 \sin \theta - 5 \cos \theta$

3–4 General reduction formulas. It is often necessary to express the circular functions of a given angle in terms of functions of an acute angle. We are able to do this by using reduction formulas obtained from (3–1). If we wish to reduce any angle by multiples of 90°, in order to work with the acute angle we recall (Problem 21, Article 2–4) that $\sin (2k \cdot 90°) = 0$ and $\cos (2k \cdot 90°) = (-1)^k$ for any integer k (positive, negative, or zero). Since

$$\sin (2k \cdot 90° + \beta) = \sin (2k \cdot 90°) \cos \beta + \cos (2k \cdot 90°) \sin \beta,$$

we have

$$\sin (2k \cdot 90° + \beta) = (-1)^k \sin \beta, \tag{3–14}$$

and similarly,

$$\cos (2k \cdot 90° + \beta) = (-1)^k \cos \beta. \tag{3–15}$$

These two relationships are for β increased or decreased by even multiples of 90°. The function is not changed although the sign may be. For odd multiples of 90°, the function is changed to its cofunction, and again the sign may also change, for

$$\sin \left[(2k + 1)\, 90° + \beta\right]$$
$$= \sin \left[90° + (2k \cdot 90° + \beta)\right]$$
$$= \sin 90° \cos (2k \cdot 90° + \beta) + \cos 90° \sin (2k \cdot 90° + \beta)$$
$$= \cos (2k \cdot 90° + \beta),$$

and therefore, by (3–15),

$$\sin \left[(2k + 1)\, 90° + \beta\right] = (-1)^k \cos \beta. \qquad (3\text{–}16)$$

Moreover,

$$\cos \left[(2k + 1)\, 90° + \beta\right]$$
$$= \cos \left[90° + (2k \cdot 90° + \beta)\right]$$
$$= \cos 90° \cos (2k \cdot 90° + \beta) - \sin 90° \sin (2k \cdot 90° + \beta)$$
$$= -(-1)^k \sin \beta,$$

and thus,

$$\cos \left[(2k + 1)\, 90° + \beta\right] = (-1)^{k+1} \sin \beta. \qquad (3\text{–}17)$$

The special case of (3–14) and (3–15), where k has the value 2, is important, since

$$\sin (\beta + 2\pi) = \sin \beta, \qquad (3\text{–}18)$$

and

$$\cos (\beta + 2\pi) = \cos \beta. \qquad (3\text{–}19)$$

It was for this reason that these functions were called *periodic* functions, with periods of 2π. [Recall Eqs. (2–12, 13).]

EXAMPLE 1. Express sin 624° as a function of a positive acute angle less than 45°.

Solution. Since $624° = 6 \cdot 90° + 84°$, by using (3–14) we have $\sin 624° = -\sin 84°$. From (3–2), $-\sin 84° = -\cos 6°$, and we have $\sin 624° = -\cos 6°$.

EXAMPLE 2. Express cos 1243° as a function of a positive acute angle less than 45°.

Solution. Again $1243° = 13 \cdot 90° + 73°$. Thus, using (3–17), $\cos 1243° = -\sin 73°$, and by (3–2), we have $\cos 1243° = -\cos 17°$.

EXAMPLE 3.   Repeat Examples 1 and 2 for cos $(-497°)$.

Solution.   Since $-497° = -5 \cdot 90° - 47°$, we have cos $(-497°)$ $= -\sin 47° = -\cos 43°$.

Having done several exercises of this type, one should be able to write the answer without the use of Formulas (3–14) through (3–17). Draw a figure, choose the sign of the function value to be simplified, depending upon the quadrant, and with this sign write the corresponding acute angle. In considering Example 1, since 624° is in the third quadrant, sin 624° is negative, and the corresponding acute angle is 84°.   Thus sin 624° $= -\sin 84°$.

PROBLEMS

Express each of the following as a function of a positive acute angle less than 45°:

1. sin 196°	2. cos 147°	3. sin 319°
4. cos 254°	5. tan 294°	6. cos 728°
7. sin $(-625°)$	8. cos $(-435°)$	9. tan 1004°
10. sin 248°25′	11. cos 106°18′	12. tan 163°17′
13. cos 204°46′	14. tan 136°34′	15. sin 156°39′

By using (3–1) or (3–9) through (3–13) show that each of the following statements is true.   Check those involving sines or cosines by (3–14) through (3–17).

16. $\sin (180° + \theta) = -\sin \theta$

17. $\cos (180° + \theta) = -\cos \theta$

18. $\sin (180° - \theta) = \sin \theta$.   *Hint:* $180° - \theta = 180° + (-\theta)$.

19. $\cos (180° - \theta) = -\cos \theta$

20. $\tan (270° - \theta) = \cot \theta$

21. $\cos (\theta - 180°) = -\cos \theta$

22. $\cos (270° + \theta) = \sin \theta$

23. $\sin (\theta + 270°) = -\cos \theta$

24. $\tan (180° + \theta) = \tan \theta$

25. $\cos (360° - \theta) = \cos \theta$

26. $\sin (360° - \theta) = -\sin \theta$

27. In Problem 24, we showed that $\tan (\theta + \pi) = \tan \theta$.   This was proved as a special case of (2–14) with $k = 1$.   What is the period of tan θ?

28. What are the periods of the cotangent, secant, and cosecant functions?

CHAPTER 4

SOLUTION OF TRIANGLES

The entire point of view with regard to solving triangles has changed during the last few years. Many numerical methods, numerous formulas, and detailed study with large numbers of exercises had been considered an important part of trigonometry. More recently, however, the analytic part of trigonometry with its applications in advanced mathematics and science has become more important. Moreover, new developments are constantly being made, resulting in extremely accurate graphical methods as well as the use of high-speed numerical calculators. We shall concentrate our attention on the fundamental theorems, and not emphasize long and detailed processes, although the tables in the back of the book will be used. There is also an appendix which explains the use of these tables. The student should read this and do a sufficient number of the problems to familiarize himself with the tables before he continues in this chapter. Such a background will be assumed.

*4-1 Circular function tables. In Chapter 2 we computed the values of the circular functions for certain angles. Considering $60° = \pi/3$ radians, we found $\cos 60° = .5000$, an exact decimal value, while $\sin 60° = \sqrt{3}/2$ and $\tan 60° = \sqrt{3}$ could be approximated as decimal values to whatever accuracy we wished. Such approximations from exact values, expressed in radicals, can be obtained only in special cases.

To find the values of the functions for any angle, we might draw the angle using a protractor and find approximate values with a scale to measure distances. Because of inaccuracies in drawing and measuring, such a method has definite limitations. The general method for finding the values of the functions to any degree of accuracy, based on calculus, is beyond the scope of this book.

We are able to find exact values of the functions for angles of every 3°, however, by a completely elementary process, and although this method is not an efficient way of obtaining the values for a table, it has sufficient mathematical interest to warrant this discussion. By combining the exact values of the functions for $\theta = 30°$, 36°, 45°, 60°, and 90°, which we found in Chapter 2, and using some of the relations of Chapter 3, we obtain our results.

Let us find exact values for sin 3° and cos 3°. By applying the values found for cos 36° (Article 2–6) to Problems 31 and 32, Article 3–3, we have

$$\sin 18° = \sqrt{\frac{1 - \cos 36°}{2}} = \sqrt{\frac{3 - \sqrt{5}}{8}},$$

and

$$\cos 18° = \sqrt{\frac{1 + \cos 36°}{2}} = \sqrt{\frac{5 + \sqrt{5}}{8}}.$$

Also, from Example 2 and Problem 2, Article 3–3, we have

$$\sin 15° = \frac{\sqrt{6} - \sqrt{2}}{4},$$

and

$$\cos 15° = \frac{\sqrt{6} + \sqrt{2}}{4}.$$

Since 18° − 15° = 3°, using (3–11),

$$\sin 3° = \sin(18° - 15°)$$
$$= \sin 18° \cos 15° - \cos 18° \sin 15°$$
$$= \sqrt{\frac{3 - \sqrt{5}}{8}} \frac{\sqrt{6} + \sqrt{2}}{4} - \sqrt{\frac{5 + \sqrt{5}}{8}} \frac{\sqrt{6} - \sqrt{2}}{4}$$
$$= \sqrt{\frac{(3 - \sqrt{5})(8 + 4\sqrt{3})}{32}} - \sqrt{\frac{(5 + \sqrt{5})(8 - 4\sqrt{3})}{32}},$$

so that

$$\sin 3°$$
$$= \frac{\sqrt{12 - 2\sqrt{15} - 4\sqrt{5} + 6\sqrt{3}} - \sqrt{20 - 2\sqrt{15} + 4\sqrt{5} - 10\sqrt{3}}}{8}.$$

$$(4\text{--}1)$$

In a similar way, using (3–1),

$$\cos 3°$$
$$= \frac{\sqrt{20 + 2\sqrt{15} + 4\sqrt{5} + 10\sqrt{3}} + \sqrt{12 + 2\sqrt{15} - 4\sqrt{5} - 6\sqrt{3}}}{8}.$$

$$(4\text{--}2)$$

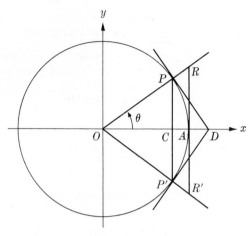

FIGURE 4-1

The values of the other functions can be found from these exact values. Of course, approximated decimal values can also be obtained to any degree of accuracy desired.

The functions of other angles could be handled similarly. For example, $6° = 36° - 30°$, $9° = 45° - 36°$, $12° = 30° - 18°$, and so on. The purpose of this discussion has been to demonstrate how a workable table could be constructed by a completely elementary process.

It is also interesting to note, although the proof will not be given, that the same angle, the angles of n degrees, with n an integral multiple of 3, are exactly those which are constructible with ruler and compass.

In a discussion concerning the construction of circular function tables, it is interesting to consider special methods for functions of small angles. By recalling the definition for $\sin \theta$ and $\tan \theta$, and restricting θ to a small positive value, we would expect the values of $\sin \theta$, $\tan \theta$, and θ to be approximately the same. This is actually the case, for consider Fig. 4-1 involving a unit circle with θ in standard position. Let A and P be the points where the initial and terminal sides of θ intersect the circle. The line from P is drawn perpendicular to the x-axis, intersecting the circle at P'. The x-axis bisects the vertical chord $P'P$ at C and the arc $\overset{\frown}{P'P}$ at A. The tangent to the circle at A is drawn, intersecting the two lines OP and OP' (extended) at R and R' respectively. The tangents to the circle at P and P' are drawn intersecting at D, a point on the x-axis. (Why?) Consider the chord $P'CP$, the arc $\overset{\frown}{P'AP}$, and the segments of the tangents to the circle, $P'D$ and DP. From a proposition in plane geometry,

$$P'CP < \overset{\frown}{P'AP} < P'DP.$$

Dividing these lengths by 2,

$$CP < \overset{\frown}{AP} < DP.$$

But $DP = AR$. (Why?) Therefore,

$$CP < \overset{\frown}{AP} < AR,$$

or

$$\sin \theta < \theta < \tan \theta. \tag{4-3}$$

This inequality will enable us to find an approximation to the values of the sine or tangent of small values of θ.

By dividing each member of (4–3) by $\sin \theta$, we have

$$1 < \frac{\theta}{\sin \theta} < \sec \theta.$$

Considering the reciprocals,* we get

$$\cos \theta < \frac{\sin \theta}{\theta} < 1, \tag{4-4}†$$

and since $\cos \theta = \sqrt{1 - \sin^2 \theta} > \sqrt{1 - \theta^2}$ (Why?), we have

$$\sqrt{1 - \theta^2} < \frac{\sin \theta}{\theta} < 1,$$

or

$$\theta\sqrt{1 - \theta^2} < \sin \theta < \theta. \tag{4-5}$$

This inequality can be used in connection with the sine function.

---

* For any number $a \neq 0$, we recall that its reciprocal is $1/a$. If $a < b$, where a and b are positive, $1/a > 1/b$.

† Consider inequality (4–4). As θ becomes smaller and smaller (approaches 0), $\cos \theta$ approaches 1. Thus $\sin \theta/\theta$, as θ approaches 0, is always between 1 and a number approaching 1. Therefore, the ratio must approach 1. This is written $\lim_{\theta \to 0} \sin \theta/\theta = 1$, and is read: the limit of $\sin \theta/\theta$, as θ approaches zero, is one. This is an extremely important result in more advanced mathematics.

Again, by dividing each member of (4–3) by tan θ, we have

$$\cos \theta < \frac{\theta}{\tan \theta} < 1, \tag{4–6}$$

or

$$\sqrt{1 - \theta^2} < \frac{\theta}{\tan \theta} < 1.$$

Using the reciprocal relation, this becomes

$$1 < \frac{\tan \theta}{\theta} < \frac{1}{\sqrt{1 - \theta^2}}, \tag{4–7}$$

or

$$\theta < \tan \theta < \frac{\theta}{\sqrt{1 - \theta^2}}. \tag{4–8}$$

Relations (4–5) and (4–8) give us bounds for $\sin \theta$ and $\tan \theta$.

EXAMPLE.   Find an approximate value of $\sin \pi/60$.

Solution.   Substituting in (4–5) for $\theta = \pi/60$, where $\pi = 3.1416$, we find

$$.05229 < \sin \pi/60 < .05236.$$

Thus, correct to four decimal places, $\sin \pi/60 = .0523$.   Notice the value listed in Table I.

It is also possible to find the value of $\cos \theta$, for small positive values of θ.   Since $\cos \theta = 1 - 2\sin^2(\theta/2)$ (Problem 29, Article 3–3), we have

$$\cos \theta > 1 - 2\frac{\theta^2}{4},$$

and thus,

$$1 > \cos \theta > 1 - \frac{\theta^2}{2}. \tag{4–9}$$

PROBLEMS

1. Establish (4–2) of this section.

2. Express 21°, 24°, and 27° by using combinations similar to those above, which might be used to find their sines or cosines.

3. Do the same for 33°, 39°, and 42°.

4. If you have access to a computing machine, find the decimal approximation for $\sin 3°$ and $\cos 3°$, using (4–1) and (4–2). Check your results with the value given in Table I.

5. Using $\pi = 3.1416$, find the best possible approximation for $\sin \pi/30$, $\cos \pi/30$, and $\tan \pi/30$, using the above inequalities.

6. Find approximations for $\cos \pi/60$ and $\tan \pi/60$. Compare these values with those given in Table I.

7. Using formula (4–7) of Article 4–1, show that $\lim\limits_{\theta \to 0} \tan \theta/\theta = 1$.

8. Using (4–4) and (4–6), prove the inequality

$$\cos \theta < \frac{\sin \theta}{\tan \theta} < 1.$$

Hint: Multiply each member of the inequality (4–6) by $\sin \theta/\theta$.

9. Using the result of Problem 8, prove $\lim\limits_{\theta \to 0} \dfrac{\sin \theta}{\tan \theta} = 1$.

10. With the use of (4–4) and (4–9), obtain the bounds for $\sin \theta$:

$$\theta \left(1 - \frac{\theta^2}{2}\right) < \sin \theta < \theta.$$

This inequality does not involve a square root, and thus has advantages in certain cases.

11. Recall from plane geometry the expression for the perimeter P of a regular n-gon inscribed in a circle of radius r, $P = 2nr \sin (\pi/n)$, and $\lim\limits_{n \to \infty} P = 2\pi r$ (the limit of the perimeter of a regular n-gon as the number of sides increases indefinitely is the circumference, $2\pi r$). Set up a limit by eliminating P from these two expressions and, by substituting $\theta = \pi/n$, prove $\lim\limits_{\theta \to 0} \sin \theta/\theta = 1$.

4–2 General discussion. If a certain number of the sides and angles of a triangle are known, the *triangle* can be *solved* by finding the remaining parts. We shall derive two of the many formulas used in solving triangles, and consider certain special cases. Other formulas and relations between the sides and angles of a triangle appear in the examples and problems.

While deriving these relations, it is important to recall that a triangle is determined when

(1) two angles and one side are given,

(2) two sides and the included angle are given,

(3) three sides are given, if the longest side is less than the sum of the other two.

Also, there are at most two triangles when

(4) two sides and an angle opposite one of them is given.

These are the four types of problems we wish to solve. We shall denote the three angles at the vertices of any triangle ABC by α, β, and γ, respectively, and the corresponding opposite sides by a, b, and c.

4–3 The Law of Sines. Let us first derive the *Law of Sines*. By choosing a rectangular coordinate system so that the angle α of the triangle ABC is in standard position (see Fig. 4–2), the coordinates of B are $(c \cos \alpha,\ c \sin \alpha)$. (Recall Problem 53, Article 2–3.) If, however, the origin of the coordinate system is at C, with $(180° - \gamma)$ in standard position, the coordinates of B are

$$[a \cos (180° - \gamma),\ a \sin (180° - \gamma)].$$

Since in either case the y-coordinates of B are equal (the same distance above the x-axis), we have

$$c \sin \alpha = a \sin(180° - \gamma)$$
$$= a \sin \gamma.$$

Dividing each member of this equation by $\sin \alpha \sin \gamma$, we obtain

$$\frac{c}{\sin \gamma} = \frac{a}{\sin \alpha}.$$

With a different choice of the x-axis, $b/\sin \beta = a/\sin \alpha$, so that

$$\frac{a}{\sin \alpha} = \frac{b}{\sin \beta} = \frac{c}{\sin \gamma}. \qquad (4\text{–}10)$$

This relationship enables us to solve the problems mentioned in (1) and (4) of Article 4–2. However, before we consider problems

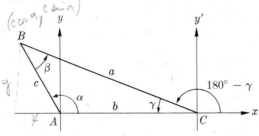

FIGURE 4–2

solved by (4–10) in general, let us consider an extremely important special case.

4–4 Solution of right triangles. If γ is a right angle equal to 90°, in (4–10), the equations reduce to $\sin \alpha = a/c$, and $\sin \beta = b/c$. But with $\gamma = 90°$, and $\alpha + \beta + \gamma = 180°$, $\beta = 90° - \alpha$, so that $\cos \alpha = b/c$. Since $\tan \alpha = \sin \alpha/\cos \alpha$, we also have $\tan \alpha = a/b$. Thus, in any right triangle with $\gamma = 90°$,

$$\sin \alpha = \frac{a}{c} = \frac{\text{side opposite } \alpha}{\text{hypotenuse}}, \qquad (4\text{–}11)$$

$$\cos \alpha = \frac{b}{c} = \frac{\text{side adjacent } \alpha}{\text{hypotenuse}}, \qquad (4\text{–}12)$$

$$\tan \alpha = \frac{a}{b} = \frac{\text{side opposite } \alpha}{\text{side adjacent } \alpha}. \qquad (4\text{–}13)$$

Before attempting to solve any triangles, the following remarks are pertinent.

1. Results can be no more accurate than the given sides and angles. We shall agree to set up the following table for accuracy between sides and angles.

Significant figures for sides:	Angles to the nearest:
2	degree
3	ten minutes
4	minute
5	tenth of a minute

2. If the results are required to only two or possibly three significant digits, the slide rule should be used for the computation. Also, the slide rule can be employed as a check upon the work, although the answers may be desired more accurately than the slide rule will allow.

3. If the results are to be correct to several significant digits, the tables should be used. When calculating machines are available, the natural functions and arithmetical methods are usually employed. Since the majority of students do not have access to machines, the logarithmic solution is the logical one. This will be illustrated in most of the examples.

4. In solving any problem it is advisable to draw the triangle, label the known parts, and make a complete systematic outline to follow, before any computation is done.

EXAMPLE 1. In the right triangle ABC, $b = 47.25$, $\alpha = 41°19'$. Find the remaining parts and the area.

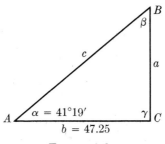

FIGURE 4-3

Solution. We first draw the triangle and label numerically the parts that are given, as in Fig. 4-3. Then $\beta = 90° - \alpha = 48°41'$. To find a, we use the relation $\tan \alpha = a/b$, and to find c, we use $\cos \alpha = b/c$.

$$a = 47.25 \tan 41°19' \qquad\qquad c = \frac{47.25}{\cos 41°19'}$$

$\log 47.25 = 1.6744$	$\log 47.25 = 11.6744 - 10$
$(+) \log \tan 41°19' = 9.9440 - 10$	$(-) \log \cos 41°19' = 9.8757 - 10$
$\log a = 11.6184 - 10$	$\log c = 1.7987$
$a = 41.54$	$c = 62.90$

The area of the triangle is $K = \frac{1}{2}ab$.

$\log 41.53 = 1.6183$	$(-) \log 2 = .3010$
$(+) \log 47.25 = 1.6744$	$\log K = 2.9917$
3.2927	$K = 981.0$

This example illustrates a problem with its results correct to four significant figures, as in Table III.

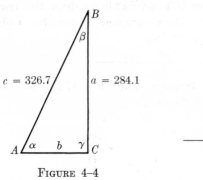

FIGURE 4-4

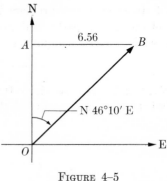

FIGURE 4-5

EXAMPLE 2. Solve the right triangle in which $a = 284.1$ and $c = 326.7$.

Solution. Draw the triangle and label numerically the parts that are known, as in Fig. 4-4. Since a and c are given, we use the relation $\sin \alpha = a/c$ to find α, and then $\cos \alpha = b/c$ to find b.

$$\sin \alpha = \frac{284.1}{326.7}$$

$$b = 326.7 \cos 60°24'$$

$$
\begin{aligned}
\log 284.1 &= 12.4534 - 10 \\
(-) \log 326.7 &= \ \ 2.5141 \\
\hline
\log \sin \alpha &= \ \ 9.9393 - 10 \\
\alpha &= 60°24' \\
\beta &= 29°36'
\end{aligned}
$$

$$
\begin{aligned}
\log 326.7 &= \ \ \ \ \ 2.5141 \\
(+) \log \cos 60°24' &= \ \ \ \ \ 9.6937 - 10 \\
\hline
\log b &= 12.2078 - 10 \\
b &= 161.4
\end{aligned}
$$

Log cos α can be found in the table when log sin α is located. This is one of the advantages in first arranging the work systematically.

In science and engineering, physical entities such as velocity, acceleration, or force not only require magnitude but also direction for their complete determination. They are represented by line segments with an arrowhead on one end to show direction, while the length of the segment, by reference to some scale, denotes magnitude. Such line segments are called *vectors*. For example, with a scale of 40 lb to the unit, the vector in Fig. 4-6 might represent a force of 200 lb acting in the direction of 60° with the positive x-axis. A

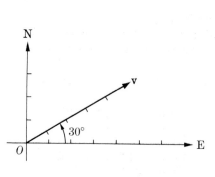

FIGURE 4–6   FIGURE 4–7

bold-face letter **v** will denote the vector, while its *length* will be designated by the ordinary v.

Since **v**, with its initial point at O, as in Fig. 4–7, has v for its length and makes an angle θ with the positive x-axis, its terminal point P has coordinates $(v \cos \theta, v \sin \theta)$. These coordinates, denoted by v_x and v_y, are called the x- and y-*components* of **v** and satisfy the relations:

$$v_x = v \cos \theta, \qquad v^2 = v_x{}^2 + v_y{}^2,$$

$$v_y = v \sin \theta, \qquad \tan \theta = \frac{v_y}{v_x}.$$

$$(4\text{–}14)$$

EXAMPLE 3. Find v_x and v_y for the vector with $v = 247$ and $\theta = 37°40'$.

Solution. $v_x = 247 \cos 37°40' = (247)(.7916) = 196.$
$v_y = 247 \sin 37°40' = (247)(.6111) = 151.$

By considering $\mathbf{v}_x$ and $\mathbf{v}_y$ as vectors, we can think of **v** as the single vector equivalent to these two. More generally, a vector **v** is the *resultant* or *sum* of two vectors $\mathbf{v}_1$ and $\mathbf{v}_2$ if, as a single force, it will produce the same result as the two forces acting together. If $\mathbf{v}_1$ and $\mathbf{v}_2$ are two nonparallel vectors emanating from the same point, their resultant **v** is the vector from that point, having the length and direction of the diagonal of the parallelogram determined by $\mathbf{v}_1$ and $\mathbf{v}_2$. (What would **v** be if $\mathbf{v}_1$ and $\mathbf{v}_2$ were parallel?) This notion is first used in Problem 22.

PROBLEMS

In solving the problems, a calculating machine should be used for some of the computations if possible. Logarithms should be used for others. All solutions should be checked.

1. Find the unknown sides and angles of each of the following triangles. In each $\gamma = 90°$.

(a) $\alpha = 37°20'$, $a = 243$ (b) $\alpha = 62°40'$, $b = 796$

(c) $a = 3.28$, $b = 5.74$ (d) $b = 68.4$, $c = 96.2$

(e) $\beta = 51°10'$, $c = 0.832$ (f) $\alpha = 37°40'$, $a = 54.8$

(g) $a = 37.9$, $b = 57.3$ (h) $\beta = 41°25'$, $c = 3265$

(i) $a = 5429$, $c = 6294$ (j) $a = 3.273$, $b = 7.647$

(k) $\beta = 62°57'$, $a = 0.8263$ (l) $\beta = 47°23'$, $b = 72.55$

(m) $b = 3572$, $c = 4846$ (n) $\alpha = 24°47'$, $b = 318.4$

2. In a circle of radius 96.4 inches, what is the central angle that subtends a chord of 40.3 inches?

3. A rectangular lot is 102 ft by 296 ft. Find the length of the diagonal and the angles it makes with the longest side.

4. A telegraph pole is held to the ground by wires 18.6 ft up the pole. Find the length of one of the wires that makes an angle of $26°20'$ with the vertical.

5. Find the area of a parallelogram whose sides are 33.7 and 15.2 inches if the angle between them is $67°40'$.

6. One of the equal sides of an isosceles triangle is 6.73 inches, and one of the base angles is $27°10'$. Find the base and altitude.

7. A 36-ft ladder is used to reach the top of a 28-ft wall. If the ladder extends 2 ft past the top of the wall, find its inclination to the horizontal.

8. A hemispherical bowl of inside radius 8.00 inches is standing level and is filled with water to a depth of 2.00 inches. Through what angle may it be tilted before the water spills?

9. A piece of wire 24.78 inches long is bent so as to form an isosceles triangle with one angle $97°26'$. Find the length of each side of the triangle formed.

10. From a point on the ground 152.3 ft away from the foot of a flag pole, the angle of elevation of the top of the pole is $31°46'$. How high is the flag pole? *Hint:* The *angle of elevation* of an object is the angle between the line of sight from the eye to the object and the horizontal, when the object observed is above the horizontal plane. When the object observed is below this horizontal plane, the angle is called the *angle of depression*.

11. From a lighthouse 75.3 ft above the level of the water, the angle of depression of a boat is $23°40'$. How far is the boat from a point at water level directly under the point of observation?

12. Find the height of a balloon directly above a town A, if the angle of depression of town B, 6.23 miles from A, is 15°20′.

13. From a lookout tower 80.0 ft high a man observes from a position 6.5 ft below the top of the tower, that the angle of elevation of the top of a certain tree is 12°40′, and the angle of depression of its base is 72°20′. If the base of the tower and tree are at the same level, what is the height of the tree?

14. From a point 20.75 ft above the surface of the water, the angle of elevation of a building at the edge of the water is 38°16′, while the angle of depression of its image in the water is 56°28′. Find the height of the building, and the horizontal distance from the point of observation.

15. From a mountain 1780 ft high the angle of depression of a point on the nearer shore of a river is 48°40′, and of a point directly across on the opposite side, the angle of depression is 22°20′. What is the width of the river between the two points?

16. At a certain point the angle of elevation of a mountain peak is 40°20′. At a point 9560 ft farther away in the same horizontal plane, its angle of elevation is 29°50′. Find the distance of the peak above the horizontal plane.

17. Lighthouse B is 6.56 miles directly east of lighthouse A. A ship at O observes that A is due north, and that the bearing of OB is N 46°10′ E. How far is the ship from A? From B? *Hint:* The *bearing* of a line in a horizontal plane is the acute angle made by this line with a north-south line. In giving the bearing of a line, the letter N or S is written, followed by the letter E or W. Thus, in Fig. 4–5, the bearing of OB is read north, 46°10′ east.

18. An airplane is 115 miles due east of a radio station A; a second radio station is 136 miles due north of A. What are the distance and bearing of the second radio station from the airplane?

19. Because of a certain wind, a boat sails 4728 ft in the direction S 47°29′ W. How far south has it gone? How far west has it gone?

20. Find v_x and v_y for each of the vectors with v and θ given:

(a) $v = 75$, $\theta = 60°$ (b) $v = 48$, $\theta = 136°$

(c) $v = 4.72$, $\theta = 217°10′$ (d) $v = 58.47$, $\theta = 47°18′$

21. Find the length and direction for each of the vectors if

(a) $v_x = 3$, $v_y = 4$ (b) $v_x = 23$, $v_y = 45$

(c) $v_x = -16.2$, $v_y = 28.7$ (d) $v_x = 382.4$, $v_y = -768.3$

22. If a force of 658.4 lb is acting east, and another of 316.2 lb is acting north, what are the magnitude and direction of their resultant?

23. A balloon is rising at the rate of 12 ft/sec and at the same time is being blown horizontally by a wind traveling 18 ft/sec. Find the angle its path makes with the vertical, and determine its actual velocity.

24. A river runs directly east at 1.28 mi/hr. If a swimmer can swim at the rate of 1.75 mi/hr in still water, and he starts swimming so that he is headed north directly across the river, in what direction is he actually swimming? Where does he hit the opposite bank if the river is one mile wide?

25. In what direction should the swimmer in Problem 24 head in order to reach a point directly across the river?

26. An airplane travels with a speed of 145 mi/hr in calm air. The wind is blowing with a velocity of 23 mi/hr from N 27° E. (a) If the plane is headed in a direction N 63° W, find the magnitude of the speed, and the direction of the airplane with reference to the ground. (b) In what direction must the airplane be headed in order to fly in the direction N 63° W, and what would be its actual speed in the air?

27. Find the resultant of the following sets of forces, where f is the magnitude and θ the angle each force makes with the positive x-axis:

(a) $f_1 = 15$, $\theta_1 = 65°$, $f_2 = 37$, $\theta_2 = 142°$
(b) $f_1 = 6280$, $\theta_1 = 37°10'$, $f_2 = 2840$, $\theta_2 = -16°40'$
(c) $f_1 = 6800$, $\theta_1 = 210°$, $f_2 = 7200$, $\theta_2 = 315°$, $f_3 = 5600$, $\theta_3 = 90°$

Note: Although we could find the resultant as the diagonal of the parallelogram, it is simpler in such problems to work with components. Obtain the sum of the x-components as one force, the sum of the y-components as another, and then find the resultant of these two.

28. The circle with center at O in Fig. 4–8 is circumscribed about the triangle and OD is drawn perpendicular to BC. What is the relation of $\angle BOD$ to α? Using the right triangle BDO, prove $\sin \alpha = a/2R$. With the necessary additional construction, prove the Law of Sines.

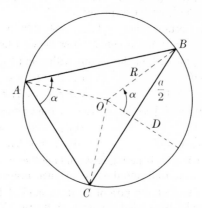

FIGURE 4–8

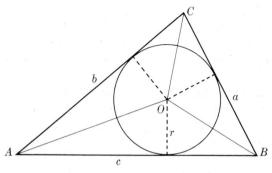

FIGURE 4–9

29. In the right triangle ABC, with $\alpha = 30°$, $AB = 2$. D is chosen on AC, so that $DC = BC$, and from D a line is drawn perpendicular to AB, meeting AB at K. Show $\angle DBK = 15°$, and by finding the lengths of the various lines, prove

$$\sin 15° = \frac{\sqrt{6} - \sqrt{2}}{4}.$$

30. Using Fig. 4–9, where the inscribed circle in triangle ABC has r for its radius, prove the area $K = rs$, where $s = (a + b + c)/2$.

4–5 The Law of Cosines.   Before considering examples in which we use the Law of Sines to solve general triangles, we shall prove another important relationship, the *Law of Cosines*.

Refer to Fig. 4–2, where the angle α of the triangle ABC is in standard position, with the vertex C at $(b,0)$. Recalling that the coordinates of B are $(c \cos \alpha, c \sin \alpha)$, we have, using (1–5), the distance between $B(c \cos \alpha, c \sin \alpha)$ and $C(b,0)$:

$$\sqrt{(c \cos \alpha - b)^2 + (c \sin \alpha - 0)^2}.$$

But this length is the length of a, so that

$$a = \sqrt{c^2 \cos^2 \alpha - 2bc \cos \alpha + b^2 + c^2 \sin^2 \alpha},$$

or

$$a^2 = b^2 + c^2 - 2bc \cos \alpha. \qquad (4\text{–}15)$$

Similarly, we obtain

$$b^2 = a^2 + c^2 - 2ac \cos \beta, \qquad (4\text{–}16)$$

$$c^2 = a^2 + b^2 - 2ab \cos \gamma. \qquad (4\text{–}17)$$

These three relations, called the Law of Cosines, hold for all triangles, and are used to solve problems of the type (2) and (3) of Article 4–2. If $\gamma = 90°$ in (4–17), $c^2 = a^2 + b^2$. For this reason, this law is sometimes called *the generalization of the Pythagorean Theorem*.

4–6 Applications involving oblique triangles. To clarify the use of the Laws of Sines and Cosines, let us consider the following examples.

EXAMPLE 1.   Solve the triangle ABC of Fig. 4–10 if $a = 524.7$, $\beta = 46°24'$, and $\gamma = 98°41'$.

Solution.   First, $\alpha = 180° - (46°24' + 98°41') = 34°55'$. With the value of α known, we can use the Law of Sines to find b and c:

$$b = \frac{a}{\sin \alpha} \sin \beta \qquad\qquad c = \frac{a}{\sin \alpha} \sin \gamma$$

$$\log 524.7 = \ 12.7199 - 10 \qquad\qquad \log \frac{a}{\sin \alpha} = \ 2.9622$$

$$(-) \log \sin 34°55' = \ \ 9.7577 - 10 \qquad (+) \log \sin 98°41' = \ \ 9.9950 - 10$$

$$\log \frac{a}{\sin \alpha} = \ \ 2.9622 \qquad\qquad \log c = \ 12.9572 - 10$$

$$(+) \log \sin 46°24' = \ \ 9.8599 - 10 \qquad\qquad c = 906.2$$
$$\log b = \ 12.8221 - 10$$
$$b = 663.9$$

This example illustrates (1) in Article 4–2.

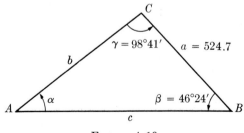

FIGURE 4–10

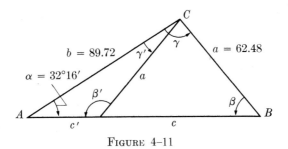

FIGURE 4-11

EXAMPLE 2. Find all the triangles with $a = 62.48$, $b = 89.72$, and $\alpha = 32°16'$.

Solution. The *ambiguous type* (4) is illustrated here. We have the possibility of two solutions, since $\sin (180° - \beta) = \sin \beta$. Using the Law of Sines, we solve for β, and find two values, for each of which there is a corresponding γ and c. Thus we have two solutions, as is suggested in Fig. 4-11.

$$\sin \beta = b \frac{\sin \alpha}{a}$$

$$\log \sin 32°16' = 9.7274 - 10$$
$$(-) \log 62.48 = 1.7958$$
$$\log \frac{\sin \alpha}{a} = 7.9316 - 10$$
$$(+) \log 89.72 = 1.9529$$
$$\log \sin \beta = 9.8845 - 10$$

$$\beta_1 = 50°2' \qquad \text{or} \qquad \beta_2 = 129°58'$$

Thus

$$\gamma_1 = 180° - (\alpha + \beta_1) \qquad \gamma_2 = 180° - (\alpha + \beta_2)$$
$$= 97°42' \qquad\qquad\qquad = 17°46'$$

Then

$$c_1 = \frac{a}{\sin \alpha} \sin \gamma_1 \qquad\qquad c_2 = \frac{a}{\sin \alpha} \sin \gamma_2$$

$$\log \frac{a}{\sin \alpha} = 2.0684 \qquad\qquad \log \frac{a}{\sin \alpha} = 2.0684$$

$$(+) \log \sin 97°41' = \underline{\quad 9.9961 - 10} \qquad (+) \log \sin 17°47' = \underline{\quad 9.4849 - 10}$$
$$\log c_1 = 12.0645 - 10 \qquad\qquad \log c_2 = 11.5533 - 10$$
$$c_1 = 116.0 \qquad\qquad\qquad c_2 = 35.75$$

EXAMPLE 3. Find the third side of the triangle with $b = 47$, $c = 58$, and $\alpha = 63°$.

Solution. For this problem, type (2) of Article 4–2, we use the Law of Cosines. It should be emphasized that using four-place tables, this law produces no more than two significant figures for the third side, since a square root is involved.

$$a^2 = (47)^2 + (58)^2 - 2 \cdot 47 \cdot 58 \cos 63°$$
$$= 2209 + 3364 - 2475.2$$
$$= 3097.8$$

Thus
$$a = 56 \text{ (approximately).}$$

The other angles could be found by using the Law of Sines.

We notice in Example 3 that the Law of Cosines does not lend itself to these problems when more than two significant figures are desired. The First Law of Tangents can be used in such cases. From the relationship $a/\sin \alpha = b/\sin \beta$, it is not difficult to show that

$$\frac{\sin \alpha - \sin \beta}{\sin \alpha + \sin \beta} = \frac{a - b}{a + b}.$$

Using this and Problem 26, Article 3–3, we have

$$\frac{\tan \frac{1}{2} (\alpha - \beta)}{\tan \frac{1}{2} (\alpha + \beta)} = \frac{a - b}{a + b}, \qquad (4\text{--}18)$$

which, together with the five similar formulas obtained by interchanging and rotating letters, are called the *First Law of Tangents.* (See Problem 7.)

EXAMPLE 4. Solve the triangle with $a = 16.47$, $b = 25.49$, and $c = 33.77$.

Solution. This example of type (3) again uses the Law of Cosines. We find

$$a^2 = \quad 271.26 \qquad 2ab = \quad 839.64$$

$$b^2 = 649.74 \qquad 2ac = 1112.4$$

$$c^2 = 1140.4 \qquad 2bc = 1721.6$$

so that

$$\cos \alpha = \frac{b^2 + c^2 - a^2}{2bc} = \quad .8823, \quad \text{or} \quad \alpha = 28°5',$$

$$\cos \beta = \frac{a^2 + c^2 - b^2}{2ac} = \quad .6850, \quad \text{or} \quad \beta = 46°46',$$

$$\cos \gamma = \frac{a^2 + b^2 - c^2}{2ab} = -.2613, \quad \text{or} \quad \beta = 105°9'.$$

This example is easily checked, since $\alpha + \beta + \gamma = 180°$.

Example 4 could be solved using five-place tables of logarithms, but the process is long, due to the form of the Law of Cosines. The *Second Law of Tangents* lends itself to large figures as well as logarithmic computation. By adding one to both members of the expression for cos α in Example 4, dividing each side by 2, and factoring the right side, we get

$$\frac{1 + \cos \alpha}{2} = \frac{(b + c + a)(b + c - a)}{4bc}.$$

Also,

$$\frac{1 - \cos \alpha}{2} = \frac{(a + b - c)(a - b + c)}{4bc}.$$

Now, letting $\dfrac{a + b + c}{2} = s$ in these expressions, and recalling Problems 31 and 32, Article 3–3, we have

$$\sin \frac{\alpha}{2} = \sqrt{\frac{(s - b)(s - c)}{bc}},$$

and

$$\cos \frac{\alpha}{2} = \sqrt{\frac{s(s - a)}{bc}}.$$

Therefore, dividing,

$$\tan \frac{\alpha}{2} = \frac{r}{s - a}, \qquad\qquad (4\text{–}19)$$

where $r = \sqrt{\dfrac{(s - a)(s - b)(s - c)}{s}}$. *

Formula (4–19) and

$$\tan \frac{\beta}{2} = \frac{r}{s - b}, \qquad \tan \frac{\gamma}{2} = \frac{r}{s - c}$$

are considered the Second Law of Tangents, and give the angles in terms of the three sides of any triangle. (See Problem 10.)

PROBLEMS

1. Solve the following triangles ABC, given

  (a) $\alpha = 62°40'$, $\beta = 79°20'$, $a = 147$
  (b) $\beta = 81°43'$, $\gamma = 57°51'$, $c = 47.35$
  (c) $\alpha = 47°57'$, $\gamma = 118°11'$, $b = 87270$
  (d) $\beta = 14°36'$, $\gamma = 53°8'$, $b = 8.367$

2. Find all the triangles with $a = 62.48$, $b = 43.17$, and $\alpha = 32°16'$ and draw the figure. Compare Example 2. *Hint:* It is impossible to have two solutions, since $\beta_2 + \alpha > 180°$.

3. Is there a triangle with $a = 62.48$, $b = 143.4$, and $\alpha = 32°16'$? Compare Example 2, and draw the figure. *Hint:* Can $\sin \beta$ be greater than one?

4. In the type of problem where two sides and an angle opposite one of these sides are given, we noticed various possibilities when the angle is less than 90°, by considering Example 2, and Problems 2 and 3. Assuming a, b, and α are given, explain the following with the aid of Fig. 4–12:

$\alpha < 90°$ $\alpha > 90°$

$a < b \sin \alpha$ gives no solution. $a \le b$ gives no solution.
$a = b \sin \alpha$ gives a special right triangle. $b < a$ gives one solution.
$b \sin \alpha < a < b$ gives two solutions.
$a \ge b$ gives one solution.

5. In each of the following either show that there is no solution or find all solutions:

  (a) $b = 59.4$, $c = 72.3$, $\beta = 38°40'$
  (b) $a = 49.3$, $c = 8.72$, $\alpha = 45°10'$
  (c) $a = 14.72$, $b = 25.64$, $\beta = 147°47'$
  (d) $b = 4.927$, $c = 5.764$, $\gamma = 57°18'$

---

* With the results of Problem 30, Article 4–4, and Problem 12 of this article, r is found to be the expression for the radius of the inscribed circle of any triangle.

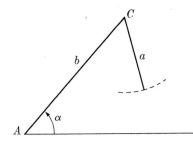
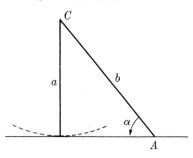
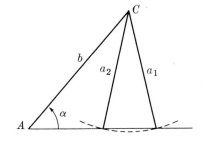
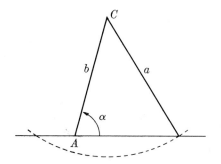

FIGURE 4–12

6. Solve each of the following triangles for the side opposite the given angle:

    (a) $a = 4$, $b = 7$, $\gamma = 30°$

    (b) $a = 7.6$, $c = 9.2$, $\beta = 47°$

    (c) $b = 8.3$, $c = 4.4$, $\alpha = 138°$

7. Solve the following triangles with

    (a) $b = 18.62$, $c = 35.61$, $\alpha = 52°18'$

Hint: Use the First Law of Tangents with $c - b = 16.99$, $c + b = 54.23$, $\frac{1}{2}(\gamma + \beta) = 63°51'$, and find $\frac{1}{2}(\gamma - \beta)$. Then $\frac{1}{2}(\gamma + \beta) + \frac{1}{2}(\gamma - \beta) = \gamma$, and so on.

    (b) $a = 463$, $b = 628$, $\gamma = 57°40'$

8. Solve the following triangles with

    (a) $a = 356.8$, $c = 551.4$, $\beta = 87°48'$

    (b) $b = 321.0$, $c = 672$, $\alpha = 124°16'$

9. Solve the following triangles by the Law of Cosines:

    (a) $a = 4$, $b = 5$, $c = 6$

    (b) $a = 32$, $b = 56$, $c = 63$

10. Solve the following triangles by the most convenient method:

(a) $a = 18.76$, $b = 25.31$, $c = 29.65$

Hint: If using logarithms and the Second Law of Tangents, arrange your work systematically:

$$2s = 73.72 \qquad\qquad \log (s - a) =$$
$$s = 36.86 \qquad\qquad \log (s - b) =$$
$$s - a = 18.10 \qquad (+)\, \log (s - c) = \underline{\qquad\qquad}$$
$$s - b = \qquad\qquad\quad \log \text{Numerator} = 3.1782$$
$$s - c = \qquad\qquad\qquad\quad (-)\, \log s = \underline{\qquad\qquad}$$
$$\log r^2 =$$
$$\log r = \quad .8058$$

$$\log r = \qquad\qquad\qquad \log r = \qquad\qquad\qquad \log r =$$
$$(-)\, \log (s - a) = \underline{\quad} \quad (-)\, \log (s - b) = \underline{\quad} \quad (-)\, \log (s - c) = \underline{\quad}$$
$$\log \tan \frac{\alpha}{2} = \qquad\qquad \log \tan \frac{\beta}{2} = \qquad\qquad \log \tan \frac{\gamma}{2} =$$
$$\frac{\alpha}{2} = \qquad\qquad\qquad \frac{\beta}{2} = \qquad\qquad\qquad \frac{\gamma}{2} =$$

(b) $a = 523$, $b = 576$, $c = 615$
(c) $a = .8147$, $b = .6834$, $c = .3449$
(d) $a = 4.32$, $b = 5.78$, $c = 13.44$

11. Considering the triangle in Fig. 4–2, prove that its area is given by the formula

$$K = \tfrac{1}{2}bc \sin \alpha.$$

Rotating the letters will also give

$$K = \tfrac{1}{2}ac \sin \beta = \tfrac{1}{2}ab \sin \gamma.$$

12. Since $\tfrac{1}{2} \sin \alpha = \sin \alpha/2 \cos \alpha/2$ (Problem 30, Article 3–3), using the values for $\sin \theta/2$ and $\cos \theta/2$, given in Problem 9, prove

$$K = \sqrt{s(s - a)(s - b)(s - c)}.$$

It is from this expression, and the result, $K = rs$, of Problem 30, Article 4–4, that we establish the value $r = \sqrt{\dfrac{(s - a)(s - b)(s - c)}{s}}$, where r is the radius of the inscribed circle.

13. Using the results of Problem 11, and the Law of Sines, show

$$K = \frac{a^2 \sin B \sin C}{2 \sin A} = \frac{b^2 \sin C \sin A}{2 \sin B} = \frac{c^2 \sin A \sin B}{2 \sin C}.$$

14. Find the areas of the triangles listed in previous problems designated by the instructor.

15. Find the lengths of the sides of a parallelogram if its diagonal, which is 72.83 inches long, makes angles with the sides of 27°52′ and 16°41′, respectively.

16. What angle does the slope of a hill make with the horizontal, if a tree 74.3 ft tall, growing on the slope of the hill, is found to subtend an angle of 19°30′ from a point 147 ft from the foot of the tree, measured along the slope straight down the hill?

17. Two airways cross each other at an angle of 49°. At a certain instant airplane A is 32 miles from the crossing, while B is 76 miles from the crossing. What is the distance between them at this instant? (Two solutions.)

18. Two sides of a parallelogram are 68 and 83 inches, and one of the diagonals is 42 inches. Find the angles of the parallelogram.

19. From a point in the same horizontal plane with the base of a building, the angles of elevation of the top and the bottom of a flagpole standing on top of the building are 64°40′ and 59°50′ respectively. If the building is 112 ft high, how tall is the flagpole?

20. As a train is traveling due north on a certain track, the engineer observes a column of smoke in a direction N 20°20′ E. After traveling 475 ft, he observes the same smoke in a direction S 71°40′ E. How far was the smoke from the first point of observation? From the second? How far was it away from the track?

21. A battleship is moving along the shoreline in a direction N 18°40′ E, at a constant rate of 36.5 mi/hr. If a squadron of airplanes which travels 186 mi/hr is due east of the battleship, in what direction should they fly in order to reach the battleship as quickly as possible?

22. If **R** is the resultant of two forces $\mathbf{f}_1$ and $\mathbf{f}_2$, and R, f_1, and f_2 represent their respective magnitudes, explain the formula $R^2 = f_1{}^2 + f_2{}^2 + 2f_1f_2 \cos \theta$, where θ is the angle between the two forces. Recall Problem 22, Article 4–4. Find the magnitude and direction of the resultant of two forces, one of 75 lb acting due north, and the other of 93 lb acting N 63° W.

23. An airplane travels with a speed of 153 mi/hr in calm air. If the wind is blowing with a velocity of 27 mi/hr from S 21° W, and the plane is headed in a direction S 53° E, find the magnitude of the speed of the airplane and its direction with reference to the ground.

24. The resultant of two forces of 61.3 lb and 34.9 lb, respectively, is a force of 73.7 lb. What angle does the resultant make with each of the two forces?

CHAPTER 5

INVERSE FUNCTIONS AND GRAPHS

A discussion of the circular functions would not be complete without presenting their inverse functions. Not only are these inverse circular functions of considerable importance and use in more advanced mathematics, but they also are helpful in clarifying certain of the properties of the circular functions. In this chapter we shall also consider the sketching of the more general circular functions.

5–1 The inverse circular functions. In considering the relation $y = \sin \theta$, we may wish to talk about y, the sine of θ, but we might also wish to consider or emphasize the angle θ, that is, θ whose sine is y. This is done so frequently that "θ an angle whose sine is y" is given a name and a notation, namely, the *inverse sine of y*, or *arcsine of y*. About 1730, Daniel Bernoulli and Leonhard Euler introduced the notation

$$\theta = \arcsin y$$

to denote an angle whose sine is y. This was the first suitable notation for an inverse circular function. Later, in 1813, John Herschel introduced another notation also in common use today, $\theta = \sin^{-1} y$. When -1 is used in this manner, it must be understood that -1 is not an exponent.

From the above definition, if $y = \arcsin 1/2$, y is an angle whose sine is $1/2$. Thus y may be equal to $\pi/6$, $5\pi/6$, $13\pi/6$, $-7\pi/6$, and so forth, or, in general, $y = \pi/6 \pm 2n\pi$, or $5\pi/6 \pm 2n\pi$, where $n = 0, 1, 2, \cdots$. Moreover, these are the only values which y may have. This will be clear from the graph of the function. From this one observation, we see that although $y = \sin x$ is a single-valued function,* the inverse function, $y = \arcsin x$, is infinitely many-valued.

The remaining inverse circular functions are defined in a corresponding way. The function arccos x denotes an angle whose cosine is x; arctan x denotes an angle whose tangent is x; and so forth. Although there are six inverse circular functions, the functions

---

* A function of x is said to be *single-valued* if to one value of x there corresponds only one value of the function. A function of x is said to be *multivalued* if two or more values of the function correspond to one value of x.

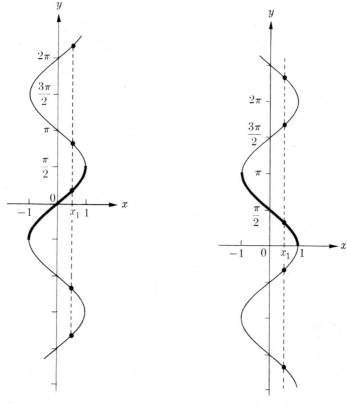

FIGURE 5–1   FIGURE 5–2

arccot x, arcsec x, and arccsc x are of less importance. They can readily be expressed in terms of arctan x, arccos x, and arcsin x, respectively, by using (2–18, 19, and 20). Thus the expression arccsc x may be considered equivalent to arcsin $1/x$. More specifically,

$$\text{arccsc } 2 = \text{arcsin } \tfrac{1}{2} = \pi/6, \text{ and so on.}$$

The graphs of the inverse circular functions show their behavior quite clearly. In considering the graph of $y = $ arcsin x, we merely think of the equivalent expression $x = \sin y$, and recall its graph. (This graph was shown in Fig. 2–10, with x and y for y and θ). If we graph $x = \sin y$ on transparent paper with the x-axis vertical and the y-axis horizontal, turn the paper over, and rotate it clockwise through 90°, the result is the graph of $y = $ arcsin x, shown in Fig. 5–1.

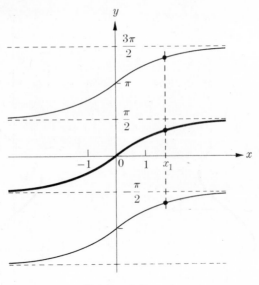

FIGURE 5-3

The graphs of $y = \text{arccos } x$ and $y = \text{arctan } x$, obtained in a similar way, are shown in Fig. 5–2 and Fig. 5–3. Notice that arcsin x and arccos x are defined only in the range where x is between -1 and 1, inclusive, although arctan x is defined for all finite values of x. Thus arcsin 2 has no meaning,* since there is no angle whose sine is 2, but arctan 2 does have meaning. We notice again, from the graphs, that these inverse functions have infinitely many values for one value of x. Observe this property in the case of each function.

If a specific value of y, let us say y_1, has its sine equal to x_1, what other values of y have the same sine? We recall that the addition or subtraction of integral multiples of 2π does not change the circular function of an angle. Also, in the case of the sine function, we found that $\sin(\pi - y) = \sin y$. Therefore $\pi - y + 2n\pi$ will have the same sine as y. In other words, an even multiple of π must be added to y, or an even multiple of π must be added to $\pi - y$ for the angle to have the same sine. Put into one equation, this results in

$$\text{arcsin } x_1 = (-1)^n y_1 + n\pi, \ (-1 \leq x_1 \leq 1), \text{ if } \sin y_1 = x_1. \quad (5\text{-}1)$$

* This is true in the present context of real values. In more advanced mathematics the circular functions may be treated in the context of complex values (see Chapter 7) and in such context arcsin 2 is a complex number.

This is true for every integral value of n and gives a different value of arcsin x_1 for each value of n.   For example, when $n = 0$, arcsin $x_1 = y$; when $n = 1$, arcsin $x_1 = \pi - y$; when $n = -1$, arcsin $x_1 = -(\pi + y_1)$; and so forth.   Also, the formula gives every value of arcsin x_1, which should be clear from Fig. 5–1.   These are indicated by the intersection of the dotted vertical line and the curve.

Since $\cos(2\pi + y) = \cos y$, and $\cos(-y) = \cos y$, it is easy to verify that the expression

$$\text{arccos } x_1 = \pm y_1 + 2n\pi, \ (-1 \leq x_1 \leq 1), \text{ if } \cos y_1 = x_1, \quad (5\text{–}2)$$

gives all the values for arccos x_1.

From the fact that both $\tan(\pi + y)$ and $\tan(2\pi + y) = \tan\theta$, we get the relation

$$\text{arctan } x_1 = y_1 + n\pi, \ (-\infty \leq x_1 \leq \infty), \text{ if } \tan y_1 = x_1, \quad (5\text{–}3)$$

for all the values of arctan x_1.

As examples of such inverse functions, we notice that

$$\arcsin \frac{1}{2} = (-1)^n \frac{\pi}{6} + n\pi,$$

$$\arccos \frac{1}{2} = \pm \frac{\pi}{3} + 2n\pi,$$

$$\arctan(-1) = -\frac{\pi}{4} + n\pi,$$

where n is any integer.

5–2 Principal values.   We noticed in Article 5–1 that the inverse functions are many-valued.   Often it is desirable to restrict these functions so that they are single-valued.   This single value is called the *principal value* of the function.   The reason for the following restrictions for such values will be clear when the study of calculus is undertaken.   At this time it merely needs to be stated that these choices are the most convenient for our purpose.   The notation for the principal value is the use of the capital A in writing the Arc functions.

The range of the principal values of each of the inverse circular functions is as follows:

$$-\frac{\pi}{2} \leq \text{Arcsin } x \leq \frac{\pi}{2},$$

$$0 \leq \operatorname{Arccos} x \leq \pi,$$

$$-\frac{\pi}{2} < \operatorname{Arctan} x < \frac{\pi}{2},$$

and the graphs of these functions are indicated in the figures by heavy lines.

In the case of the principal values, the examples listed in Article 5-1 become:

Arcsin $\frac{1}{2} = \pi/6$,   Arccos $\frac{1}{2} = \pi/3$,   and Arctan $(-1) = -\pi/4$.

Some other examples of principal values are:

$$\operatorname{Arcsin}\left(-\tfrac{1}{2}\right) = -\pi/6, \qquad \operatorname{Arccot}\left(-\sqrt{3}\right) = -\pi/6,$$

$$\operatorname{Arccos}\left(-\tfrac{1}{2}\right) = 2\pi/3, \qquad \operatorname{Arcsec}\left(-2/\sqrt{3}\right) = -5\pi/6.$$

PROBLEMS

Find the values of the following without using tables:

1. Arcsin $\sqrt{3}/2$

Hint: We know sin $\pi/3 = \sqrt{3}/2$.   Therefore

$$\arcsin \sqrt{3}/2 = (-1)^n \pi/3 + n\pi.$$

2. arctan 1   3. arccos $\left(-\tfrac{1}{2}\right)$

4. arcsin 0   5. arctan 0

6. arccos (-1) 7. arcsec $\sqrt{2}$

8. arccot $-\sqrt{3}$ 9. Arccos 0

10. Arctan (-1) 11. Arcsin (-1)

12. Arccsc 2

Find the value of the following with the help of Table I:

13. arcsin 0.4067   14. arctan 1.5399

15. arccos 0.6293   16. Arccos 0.8450

17. Arcsin 0.9951   18. Arctan 0.3281

Solve each of the following for θ:

19. $y = \sin 4\theta$

Hint: We know $4\theta = \arcsin y$.   Therefore $\theta = (\arcsin y)/4$.

20. $y = \cos 3\theta$ 21. $y = 3 \tan 2\theta$

22. $y = \sin(\theta/2)$ 23. $2y = 4 \sec 2\theta$

24. $3y = 2 + \sin 3\theta$

25. Explain why the principal value of $y = \arccos x$ cannot be taken in the interval $-\pi/2 \leqslant y \leqslant \pi/2$.

Solve each of the following for x:

26. $y = \arcsin 2x$ 27. $y = \frac{1}{3} \arccos(4x - 4)$

28. $y = \arctan(x - 2)$ 29. $y = \arctan x - 2$

30. $y = \pi + 2 \arcsin x$ 31. $8y = \pi/3 - 4 \arccos(2x + 1)$

5–3 Operations involving inverse circular functions. The most convenient way of considering various operations with the inverse functions is to analyze several examples. It is sometimes clearer, since the inverse circular functions are the same angles for which we have established many formulas, to substitute for an arc function an angle θ or ω. This type of substitution will be illustrated in the examples.

EXAMPLE 1.   Find the value of $\sin(\arccos \frac{3}{5})$.

Solution. This example, similar to many problems in Chapter 2, asks for the sine of an angle whose cosine is $\frac{3}{5}$. Let θ be this angle. Then $\cos \theta = \frac{3}{5}$, and $\sin \theta = \pm\sqrt{1 - (\frac{3}{5})^2} = \pm\frac{4}{5}$.

EXAMPLE 2.   Find the value of $\cos(\text{Arcsin } u + \text{Arccos } v)$.

Solution. Letting Arcsin $u = \theta_1$ and Arccos $v = \theta_2$, the example reduces to expressing $\cos(\theta_1 + \theta_2)$ in terms of u and v, where

$$\sin \theta_1 = u, \qquad\qquad \cos \theta_2 = v,$$

and therefore,

$$\cos \theta_1 = \sqrt{1 - u^2}, \qquad \sin \theta_2 = \sqrt{1 - v^2}.$$

(Explain why both radicals are positive.)   Thus

$$\cos(\text{Arcsin } u + \text{Arccos } v) = \cos(\theta_1 + \theta_2)$$
$$= \cos \theta_1 \cos \theta_2 - \sin \theta_1 \sin \theta_2$$
$$= v\sqrt{1 - u^2} - u\sqrt{1 - v^2}.$$

EXAMPLE 3.   Prove that Arctan $\frac{1}{2}$ + Arctan $\frac{1}{3} = \pi/4$.

Solution. Since each of the two angles on the left side is less than $\pi/4$, the left side represents an angle between 0 and $\pi/2$, as does the angle $\pi/4$ on the right side. If the tangents of two such angles are equal, the angles themselves are equal. Let us take the tangent of each member of the suspected equality, and if they are equal, we have proved the original relation. It should be emphasized that this will be true only because the tangent function between 0 and $\pi/2$ is single-valued.

$$\tan \left(\text{Arctan } \tfrac{1}{2} + \text{Arctan } \tfrac{1}{3} \right) \overset{?}{=} \tan \frac{\pi}{4}$$

$$\frac{\tan \left(\text{Arctan } \tfrac{1}{2} \right) + \tan \left(\text{Arctan } \tfrac{1}{3} \right)}{1 - \tan \left(\text{Arctan } \tfrac{1}{2} \right) \tan \left(\text{Arctan } \tfrac{1}{3} \right)} \overset{?}{=} 1$$

$$\frac{\tfrac{1}{2} + \tfrac{1}{3}}{1 - \tfrac{1}{2} \cdot \tfrac{1}{3}} = 1.$$

PROBLEMS

Find the values of the following without the use of tables:

1. $\sin (\arctan 3/4)$
2. $\cos (\arcsin 7/25)$
3. $\tan (\arccos 5/13)$
4. $\sin [\arccos (-24/25)]$
5. $\cos (\text{Arcsin } 5/6)$
6. $\tan [\text{Arcsin } (-3/4)]$
7. $\sin (\arcsin u)$
8. $\cos (\text{Arccos } v)$
9. $\tan (\arccos u)$
10. $\sin (\arctan v)$
11. $\text{Arcsin } (\sin \pi/7)$
12. $\text{Arccos } [\cos (-\pi/5)]$
13. $\text{Arctan } (\cot 4\pi/9)$
14. $\text{Arcsin } (\cos \pi/7)$
15. $\text{Arccos } (\sin \pi/10)$
16. $\text{Arccot } [\tan (-\pi/5)]$
17. $\text{Arcsin } (\tan \pi)$
18. $\text{Arctan } (\sin 7\pi/2)$
19. $\sin (\arcsin u + \arccos v)$
20. $\cos (\arccos u + \arcsin v)$
21. $\sin (\arccos 4/5 + \pi)$
22. $\cos (\pi/2 - \arcsin 5/13)$
23. $\sin (\arcsin 1/4 + \arccos 1/4)$
24. $\cos (\arctan 9/40 - \arccos 15/17)$
25. $\tan [\text{Arcsin } 5/13 + \text{Arctan } (-3/4)]$
26. $\cos [\text{Arccos } (-1/2) + \text{Arcsin } (-1/3)]$
27. $\sin [2 \text{ Arcsin } 4/5 + 1/2 \text{ Arccos } 1/9]$
28. $\cos (\text{Arcsin } 3/5 + \text{Arccos } 5/13 + \text{Arctan } 8/15)$

Verify the following equations without the use of tables:

29. $\text{Arctan } 3 + \text{Arctan } 1/3 = \pi/2$
30. $\text{Arcsin } 3/5 + \text{Arccos } 12/13 = \text{Arcsin } 56/65$

5–6 Graphing by addition of ordinates. One other very useful method of sketching is the method known as *composition of ordinates.* An example will best illustrate this method. In Chapter 8 this will be used in connection with certain applications.

EXAMPLE. Sketch the graph of $y = \sin x + \sin 2x$.

Solution. This graph is drawn by first sketching on the same axes the graphs of the two separate functions $y = \sin x$ and $y = \sin 2x$. Then the ordinate for any value of x is the sum of the ordinates for that value of x from each of the graphs, $y = \sin x$ and $y = \sin 2x$. This amounts to finding the height of the curve $y = \sin x + \sin 2x$ by adding the heights of the other two curves. Of course, the sign must be taken into account. The period of one of these functions is 2π, while the other is π. Thus the period of the function $y = \sin x + \sin 2x$ is 2π. The required graph appears in Fig. 5–7.

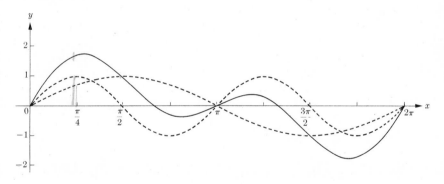

FIGURE 5–7

PROBLEMS

Sketch the graphs of the following relationships, giving their amplitudes, periods, and phase displacements:

1. $y = 2 \sin (x - \pi/6)$
2. $y = 4 \sin (x - 1)$
3. $y = 0.5 \sin (2x + \pi/8)$
4. $y = 3 \cos (t/2 - 1)$
5. $y = \sin (t + 0.25)$
6. $y = 2 \sin [(t - 1)/3]$
7. $13y = 5 \sin x + 12 \cos x$
8. $y = \sin x + \cos x$
9. $y = 15 \sin x + 8 \cos x$
10. $y = 24 \sin x + 7 \cos x$

11. $y = 2 \sin x - 5 \cos x$ 12. $y = 0.6 \sin 2x + 0.5 \cos 2x$

Sketch the graphs of the following functions, by the method of addition of ordinates, and give the period of each:

13. $y = \sin x + \cos x$ (Compare this curve with Problem 8.)

14. $y = 2 \sin x + 3 \cos 2x$ 15. $y = 4 \cos x/2 - 3 \sin 2x$

16. $y = 0.26 \sin x + 0.47 \cos 3x$ 17. $y = \sin x + \sin 2x + \sin 3x$

CHAPTER 6

IDENTITIES AND EQUATIONS

There are two types of equations in mathematics. These two, the identity and the conditional equation, will be considered as they apply to the circular functions, for both have an important place in the study and use of these functions.

6–1 The fundamental identities. An *identity* is an equation that holds true for all permissible* values of the quantities involved. In Chapters 2 and 3, many of the relationships between functions are identities, since they hold for all defined values of the functions. The following examples will help to clarify the meaning of identity. To emphasize the fact that the relations are identities, the symbol $\equiv$ will be used.

EXAMPLE 1. $x^2 - 4 \equiv (x + 2)(x - 2)$ holds for all values of x.

EXAMPLE 2. $\dfrac{x^2}{x - 3} - x \equiv \dfrac{3x}{x - 3}$ holds for all permissible values of x, since it is true for every value of x except $x = 3$. When $x = 3$, the denominator of two of the expressions is zero, and the terms do not exist.

EXAMPLE 3. $\sin^2 \theta + \cos^2 \theta \equiv 1$ holds for all values of θ.

EXAMPLE 4. The expression $\tan \theta \equiv \sin \theta / \cos \theta$ holds for all permissible values. Explain the situation when $\theta = \pi/2$.

The *fundamental circular function identities* which are given in Chapter 2 as relationships have been defined or proved but are listed again as identities for emphasis.

The reciprocal relations,

$$\sin \theta \csc \theta \equiv 1, \tag{6-1}$$

$$\cos \theta \sec \theta \equiv 1, \tag{6-2}$$

$$\tan \theta \cot \theta \equiv 1; \tag{6-3}$$

* The permissible values are all those values for which each side of the equation has meaning.

the tangent and cotangent relations,

$$\tan \theta \equiv \frac{\sin \theta}{\cos \theta} , \tag{6-4}$$

$$\cot \theta \equiv \frac{\cos \theta}{\sin \theta} ; \tag{6-5}$$

and the Pythagorean relations,

$$\sin^2 \theta + \cos^2 \theta \equiv 1, \tag{6-6}$$

$$\tan^2 \theta + 1 \equiv \sec^2 \theta, \tag{6-7}$$

$$1 + \cot^2 \theta \equiv \csc^2 \theta, \tag{6-8}$$

are called the eight *fundamental* identities in trigonometry.

With the use of these, any circular function may be expressed in terms of any other function. More specifically, for example, the identities (6-1), (6-2), (6-4), and (6-5) imply that any expression involving the circular functions of θ can be expressed in terms of $\sin \theta$ and $\cos \theta$ only. With these and (6-6) in the form $\cos \theta \equiv \pm \sqrt{1 - \sin^2 \theta}$, where the choice of the sign will depend on the quadrant of θ, any expression can be written completely in terms of $\sin \theta$.

It is, of course, possible to prove other identities than the ones just given, although there is no general rule for a procedure.

Factoring and the addition of fractions or other algebraic simplifications are often advantageous, but the introduction of radicals should be avoided whenever possible. If in doubt, it may be helpful to express all the functions in terms of sines and cosines and simplify. The establishing of an identity is accomplished by reducing (1) the left member into the exact form of the right, (2) the right into the exact form of the left, or (3) each side separately into the same form. In the following examples, give the reasons for each step.

EXAMPLE 5. By reducing the left member to the form of the right, prove that $\dfrac{1}{\sin \theta} - \sin \theta \equiv \cot \theta \cos \theta$.

Solution.

$$\frac{1}{\sin \theta} - \sin \theta \equiv \frac{1 - \sin^2 \theta}{\sin \theta}$$

$$\equiv \frac{\cos^2 \theta}{\sin \theta}$$

$$\equiv \frac{\cos \theta}{\sin \theta} \cos \theta$$

$$\equiv \cot \theta \cos \theta.$$

EXAMPLE 6.   By reducing each side separately to the same form, prove that $\tan \theta \sin \theta \equiv \sec \theta - \cos \theta$.

Solution.

$\tan \theta \sin \theta$		$\sec \theta - \cos \theta$
$\dfrac{\sin \theta}{\cos \theta} \sin \theta$		$\dfrac{1}{\cos \theta} - \cos \theta$
$\dfrac{\sin^2 \theta}{\cos \theta}$		$\dfrac{1 - \cos^2 \theta}{\cos \theta}$
$\dfrac{\sin^2 \theta}{\cos \theta}$	$\equiv$	$\dfrac{\sin^2 \theta}{\cos \theta}.$

EXAMPLE 7.   Prove the identity $\dfrac{1 - \sin \theta}{\cos \theta} \equiv \dfrac{\cos \theta}{1 + \sin \theta}.$

Solution.

$$\frac{1 - \sin \theta}{\cos \theta} \equiv \frac{(1 - \sin \theta)(1 + \sin \theta)}{\cos \theta \, (1 + \sin \theta)}$$

$$\equiv \frac{1 - \sin^2 \theta}{\cos \theta \, (1 + \sin \theta)}$$

$$\equiv \frac{\cos^2 \theta}{\cos \theta \, (1 + \sin \theta)}$$

$$\equiv \frac{\cos \theta}{1 + \sin \theta}.$$

There are three different reasons for learning to prove identities such as those in the following set of problems. By working with and proving such relationships, one more easily masters the formulas and definitions of the circular functions. One also matures mathematically through the acquisition or review of certain algebraic manipulations. Most important, however, many such identities are often employed in more advanced mathematics.

Problems

By means of the fundamental identities, express each of the following in terms of $\sin \theta$ only:

1. $\csc \theta$ 2. $\cos^2 \theta$ 3. $\cos \theta$

4. $\sec \theta$ 5. $\tan \theta$ 6. $\cot \theta$

By means of the fundamental identities, express each of the following in terms of $\cos \theta$ only:

7. $\sec \theta$ 8. $\sin^2 \theta$ 9. $\sin \theta$

10. $\csc \theta$ 11. $\tan \theta$ 12. $\cot \theta$

13. Express all six functions of θ in terms of $\tan \theta$. *Hint:* Use the identity $\sec^2 \theta \equiv 1 + \tan^2 \theta$.

14. Express $\dfrac{\sin \theta + \tan \theta}{\sec \theta + 1}$ in terms of $\sin \theta$ only.

15. Express $\dfrac{\tan \theta + \cot \theta}{\sec \theta \sin \theta}$ in terms of $\cos \theta$ only.

Prove the following identities:

16. $\tan \theta + \cot \theta \equiv \sec \theta \csc \theta$

17. $1 - 2 \sin^2 \theta \equiv 2 \cos^2 \theta - 1$

18. $\sin \theta \cos \theta \sec \theta \csc \theta \equiv 1$

19. $\dfrac{1}{1 + \sin \theta} + \dfrac{1}{1 - \sin \theta} \equiv 2 \sec^2 \theta$

20. $\cos \theta + \tan \theta \sin \theta \equiv \sec \theta$

21. $\cos^4 \theta - \sin^4 \theta \equiv \cos^2 \theta - \sin^2 \theta$

22. $\dfrac{\tan \theta - \cot \theta}{\tan \theta + \cot \theta} \equiv 2 \sin^2 \theta - 1$

23. $\dfrac{\sin \theta}{1 + \cos \theta} + \dfrac{1 + \cos \theta}{\sin \theta} \equiv 2 \csc \theta$

24. $\dfrac{1 - \cos \theta}{\sin \theta} \equiv \dfrac{\sin \theta}{1 + \cos \theta}$

25. $\cos^2 \theta - \sin^2 \theta \equiv \dfrac{1 - \tan^2 \theta}{1 + \tan^2 \theta}$

26. $\cot \theta + \tan \theta \equiv \cot \theta \sec^2 \theta$

27. $\dfrac{1 + \tan^2 \theta}{\tan^2 \theta} \equiv \csc^2 \theta$

28. $(\csc \theta - \cot \theta)^2 \equiv \dfrac{1 - \cos \theta}{1 + \cos \theta}$

29. $(\sec \theta - \tan \theta)^2 \equiv \dfrac{1 - \sin \theta}{1 + \sin \theta}$

30. $(\cos \theta - \sin \theta)^2 + 2 \sin \theta \cos \theta \equiv 1$

31. $\dfrac{\cot^2 \theta - 1}{1 + \cot^2 \theta} \equiv 2 \cos^2 \theta - 1$

32. $\dfrac{1 + \csc \theta}{\csc \theta - 1} \equiv \dfrac{1 + \sin \theta}{1 - \sin \theta}$

33. $\dfrac{\tan \theta}{1 - \cot \theta} + \dfrac{\cot \theta}{1 - \tan \theta} \equiv 1 + \tan \theta + \cot \theta$

34. $\dfrac{1 - \tan^2 \theta}{1 + \tan^2 \theta} \equiv 1 - 2 \sin^2 \theta$

35. $\dfrac{2 \sin^2 \theta - 1}{\sin \theta \cos \theta} \equiv \tan \theta - \cot \theta$

36. $\sec \theta \csc \theta - 2 \cos \theta \csc \theta \equiv \tan \theta - \cot \theta$

37. $\dfrac{\cos \theta - \sin \theta}{\cos \theta + \sin \theta} \equiv \dfrac{\cot \theta - 1}{\cot \theta + 1}$

38. $\dfrac{\sin \theta}{\csc \theta - \cot \theta} \equiv 1 + \cos \theta$

39. $\dfrac{(\cos^2 \theta - \sin^2 \theta)^2}{\cos^4 \theta - \sin^4 \theta} \equiv 1 - 2 \sin^2 \theta$

40. $\dfrac{\sec^2 \theta}{1 + \sin \theta} \equiv \dfrac{\sec^2 \theta - \sec \theta \tan \theta}{\cos^2 \theta}$

41. $1 + \cot \theta \equiv \dfrac{(1 - \cot^2 \theta) \sin \theta}{\sin \theta - \cos \theta}$

42. $\dfrac{\sec \theta + \tan \theta}{\cos \theta - \tan \theta - \sec \theta} \equiv -\csc \theta$

43. $\sin \theta + \cos \theta + \dfrac{\sin \theta}{\cot \theta} \equiv \sec \theta + \csc \theta - \dfrac{\cos \theta}{\tan \theta}$

44. $\dfrac{\sin \theta \cos \theta + \cos \theta \sin \theta}{\cos \theta \cos \theta - \sin \theta \sin \theta} \equiv \dfrac{\tan \theta + \tan \theta}{1 - \tan \theta \tan \theta}$

6–2 General identities. We recall that not only the reduction formulas but the formulas for the functions of the sum or difference of two angles (Chapter 3) were proved for any angles and, thus, holding for all angles, were actually identities. The *general addition identities* should be reviewed, and are listed below:

$$\sin (\alpha \pm \beta) \equiv \sin \alpha \cos \beta \pm \cos \alpha \sin \beta, \qquad (6\text{–}9)$$

$$\cos (\alpha \pm \beta) \equiv \cos \alpha \cos \beta \mp \sin \alpha \sin \beta, \qquad (6\text{–}10)$$

$$\tan (\alpha \pm \beta) \equiv \frac{\tan \alpha \pm \tan \beta}{1 \mp \tan \alpha \tan \beta}. \qquad (6\text{–}11)$$

These can be used to prove other identities, several of which appear in the next list of problems. Also, they are used to obtain the important double- and half-angle identities. Since they are true for any α and β, letting $\alpha = \beta$, we immediately have

$$\sin 2\alpha \equiv \sin (\alpha + \alpha)$$
$$\equiv \sin \alpha \cos \alpha + \cos \alpha \sin \alpha,$$

or

$$\sin 2\alpha \equiv 2 \sin \alpha \cos \alpha. \qquad (6\text{–}12)$$

Also,

$$\cos (\alpha + \alpha) \equiv \cos \alpha \cos \alpha - \sin \alpha \sin \alpha,$$

or

$$\cos 2\alpha \equiv \cos^2 \alpha - \sin^2 \alpha \qquad (6\text{–}13)$$

$$\equiv 1 - 2 \sin^2 \alpha \quad \text{(Why?)} \qquad (6\text{–}14)$$

$$\equiv 2 \cos^2 \alpha - 1. \quad \text{(Why?)} \qquad (6\text{–}15)$$

Moreover,

$$\tan (\alpha + \alpha) \equiv \frac{\tan \alpha + \tan \alpha}{1 - \tan \alpha \tan \alpha},$$

or

$$\tan 2\alpha \equiv \frac{2 \tan \alpha}{1 - \tan^2 \alpha}. \qquad (6\text{–}16)$$

The half-angle identities are also readily established. By using (6–14) with $2\alpha = \theta$, or $\alpha = \theta/2$,

$$\cos \theta \equiv 1 - 2 \sin^2 \frac{\theta}{2}.$$

Solving for sin $\theta/2$, we have,

$$2 \sin^2 \theta/2 \equiv 1 - \cos \theta, \tag{6–17}$$

so that

$$\sin \frac{\theta}{2} \equiv \pm \sqrt{\frac{1 - \cos \theta}{2}}, \tag{6–18}$$

where the choice of the sign before the radical is determined by the quadrant in which $\theta/2$ lies. Similarly, using (6–15) with the same substitution $\alpha = \theta/2$,

$$\cos \theta \equiv 2 \cos^2 \frac{\theta}{2} - 1,$$

and solving for $\cos \theta/2$, we get

$$2 \cos^2 \frac{\theta}{2} \equiv 1 + \cos \theta, \tag{6–19}$$

or

$$\cos \frac{\theta}{2} \equiv \pm \sqrt{\frac{1 + \cos \theta}{2}}, \tag{6–20}$$

with the choice of the sign again depending on the location of $\theta/2$.

There are two identities for $\tan \theta/2$, obtained by using (6–17) and (6–19). In the identity

$$\tan \frac{\theta}{2} \equiv \frac{\sin \theta/2}{\cos \theta/2},$$

by multiplying the numerator and denominator of the right member by $2 \sin \theta/2$, we have

$$\tan \frac{\theta}{2} \equiv \frac{2 \sin^2 \theta/2}{2 \sin \theta/2 \cos \theta/2},$$

or

$$\tan \frac{\theta}{2} \equiv \frac{1 - \cos \theta}{\sin \theta}. \tag{6–21}$$

In the same expression, multiplying by $2 \cos \theta/2$, we have

$$\tan \frac{\theta}{2} \equiv \frac{2 \sin \theta/2 \cos \theta/2}{2 \cos^2 \theta/2},$$

or

$$\tan \frac{\theta}{2} \equiv \frac{\sin \theta}{1 + \cos \theta}. \tag{6–22}$$

Some of the uses of the identities of this article will be more clearly
understood by considering the following examples.

EXAMPLE 1. Compute the value of $\sin \pi/12$ and $\cos \pi/12$ from the
functions of $\pi/6$.

Solution. Using (6–18),

$$\sin \frac{\pi}{12} = \sin \frac{1}{2} \cdot \frac{\pi}{6} = \sqrt{\frac{1 - \cos \pi/6}{2}} = \sqrt{\frac{1 - \sqrt{3}/2}{2}} = \frac{\sqrt{2 - \sqrt{3}}}{2}.$$

Also, by (6–20),

$$\cos \frac{\pi}{12} = \cos \frac{1}{2} \cdot \frac{\pi}{6} = \sqrt{\frac{1 + \cos \pi/6}{2}} = \sqrt{\frac{1 + \sqrt{3}/2}{2}} = \frac{\sqrt{2 + \sqrt{3}}}{2}.$$

EXAMPLE 2. Express $\sin 2\theta$, $\cos 2\theta$, and $\tan 2\theta$ in terms of x, if
$x = \tan \theta$.

Solution. First let us find $\sin \theta$ and $\cos \theta$ in terms of x. Since

$$\sec \theta \equiv \pm \sqrt{1 + \tan^2 \theta} \equiv \pm \sqrt{1 + x^2},$$

$$\cos \theta \equiv \pm \frac{1}{\sqrt{1 + x^2}}.$$

Also,

$$\sin \theta \equiv \tan \theta \cos \theta \equiv \pm \frac{x}{\sqrt{1 + x^2}}.$$

Therefore,

$$\sin 2\theta \equiv 2 \sin \theta \cos \theta \equiv \frac{x}{1 + x^2}.$$

A complete analysis is necessary to show that the sign in the above
example is correct, by considering θ in the first, second, third, and
fourth quadrants. Also

$$\cos 2\theta \equiv \cos^2 \theta - \sin^2 \theta \equiv \frac{1 - x^2}{1 + x^2},$$

and

$$\tan 2\theta \equiv \frac{2 \tan \theta}{1 - \tan^2 \theta} \equiv \frac{2x}{1 - x^2}.$$

EXAMPLE 3. Reduce $\sin^4 \theta$ to an expression involving only functions of θ raised to the first power.

Solution. By (6–17), we have

$$\sin^2 \theta \equiv \frac{1 - \cos 2\theta}{2} \, .$$

Thus we notice that by doubling the angle we have changed the exponent of the circular function from 2 to 1. Thus

$$\sin^4 \theta \equiv (\sin^2 \theta)^2 \equiv \frac{(1 - \cos 2\theta)^2}{4} \equiv \frac{1 - 2\cos 2\theta + \cos^2 2\theta}{4} \, ,$$

and replacing $\cos^2 2\theta$ by $\dfrac{1 + \cos 4\theta}{2}$ (Why is this possible?), we obtain

$$\sin^4 \theta \equiv \frac{3 - 4\cos 2\theta + \cos 4\theta}{8} \, .$$

This type of transformation is extremely useful in calculus.

PROBLEMS

1. Verify the identities for $\sin 2\theta$ and $\tan 2\theta$ for the value $\theta = \pi/3$.

2. Use the double-angle identities to compute $\sin 4\pi/3$, $\cos 4\pi/3$, and $\tan 4\pi/3$ from the functions of $2\pi/3$.

3. Compute $\sin 7\pi/12$, $\cos 7\pi/12$, and $\tan 7\pi/12$ from the values of the functions of $7\pi/6$.

4. If $\sin \theta = 3/5$, and θ is in the first quadrant, find the exact value of

(a) $\sin 2\theta$ (b) $\cos 2\theta$ (c) $\tan 2\theta$
(d) $\sin \theta/2$ (e) $\cos \theta/2$ (f) $\tan \theta/2$

5. If $\cos \theta = -5/13$, and θ is in the second quadrant, find the exact value of

(a) $\sin 2\theta$ (b) $\cos 2\theta$ (c) $\tan 2\theta$
(d) $\sin \theta/2$ (e) $\cos \theta/2$ (f) $\tan \theta/2$

6. Reduce $\sin^2 \theta$ to an expression involving only circular functions of θ, raised to the first power.

7. Reduce $\cos^4 \theta$ to an expression involving only circular functions of θ, raised to the first power.

8. Derive identity (6–22) by using the identity $\sin \omega/2 \equiv \sin (\omega - \omega/2)$. *Hint:* $\sin \omega/2 \equiv \sin \omega \cos \omega/2 - \cos \omega \sin \omega/2$ or $(1 + \cos \omega) \sin \omega/2 \equiv \sin \omega \cos \omega/2$.

9. Derive identity (6–21) by using the identity

$$\cos \frac{\omega}{2} \equiv \cos \left(\omega - \frac{\omega}{2} \right).$$

10. Derive the identity $\tan \dfrac{\omega}{2} \equiv \pm \sqrt{\dfrac{1 - \cos \omega}{1 + \cos \omega}}$.

11. Derive the identity $\tan \omega/2 \equiv \csc \omega - \cot \omega$.

Prove the following identities:

12. $\sin 3\theta \equiv 3 \sin \theta - 4 \sin^3 \theta$

13. $\cos 3\theta \equiv 4 \cos^3 \theta - 3 \cos \theta$

14. $\sin \dfrac{\theta}{2} \cos \dfrac{\theta}{2} \equiv \dfrac{\sin \theta}{2}$

15. $\dfrac{1 - \cos 2\theta}{\sin 2\theta} \equiv \tan \theta$

16. $\left(\cos \dfrac{\theta}{2} - \sin \dfrac{\theta}{2} \right)^2 \equiv 1 - \sin \theta$

17. $\csc 2\theta - \cot 2\theta \equiv \tan \theta$

18. $\csc 2\theta + \cot 2\theta \equiv \cot \theta$

19. $\tan 3\theta \equiv \dfrac{3 \tan \theta - \tan^3 \theta}{1 - 3 \tan^2 \theta}$

20. $\dfrac{\tan \theta/2 + \cot \theta/2}{\cot \theta/2 - \tan \theta/2} \equiv \sec \theta$

21. $\dfrac{\sin 2\theta}{\sin \theta} - \dfrac{\cos 2\theta}{\cos \theta} \equiv \sec \theta$

22. $\dfrac{\sin 3\theta}{\sin \theta} - \dfrac{\cos 3\theta}{\cos \theta} \equiv 2$

23. $\dfrac{\sin 3\theta}{\cos \theta} + \dfrac{\cos 3\theta}{\sin \theta} \equiv 2 \cot 2\theta$

24. $\dfrac{2 \tan \theta}{1 + \tan 2\theta} \equiv \sin 2\theta$

25. $\dfrac{\cot^2 \theta - 1}{\csc^2 \theta} \equiv \cos 2\theta$

26. In Fig. 6–1, A is the mid-point of an arc of the unit circle subtended by a central angle θ. Using this figure, where $\theta < \pi$, and (2–25), show $\sin \dfrac{\theta}{2} \equiv \sqrt{\dfrac{1 - \cos \theta}{2}}$.

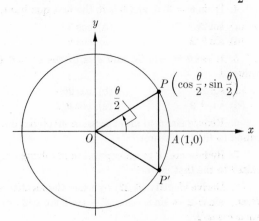

FIGURE 6–1

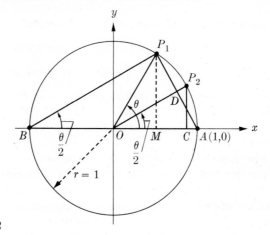

FIGURE 6–2

27. In the unit circle in Fig. 6–2, P_2 is the mid-point of the arc $\overset{\frown}{AP_1}$, cut by the central angle θ. BP_1 is drawn parallel to OP_2, so that $< P_1BA = \angle P_2OA = \theta/2$. (Why?)

(a) Verify that $BP_1 \equiv 2 \cos \theta/2$ and $P_1A = 2 \sin \theta/2$. *Hint:* $CP_2 = AD = P_1A/2$, and $OC = OD = BP_1/2$.

(b) Verify from the figure that $\sin \theta = 2 \sin \theta/2 \cos \theta/2$.

(c) Verify from the figure that $\sin \dfrac{\theta}{2} = \sqrt{\dfrac{1 - \cos \theta}{2}}$.

(d) Verify from the figure that $\cos \dfrac{\theta}{2} = \sqrt{\dfrac{1 + \cos \theta}{2}}$.

6–3 Conversions of sums and products. It is quite often necessary to convert a product of two circular functions into a sum of two functions, and vice versa. This is possible by employing the identities (6–9, 10). The following identities are not as important as the previous ones in this chapter. By adding the members of the two identities given by (6–9),

$$\sin(\alpha + \beta) + \sin(\alpha - \beta) \equiv 2 \sin \alpha \cos \beta,$$

or

$$\sin \alpha \cos \beta \equiv \tfrac{1}{2}[\sin(\alpha + \beta) + \sin(\alpha - \beta)]. \qquad (6\text{–}23)$$

By subtracting, we obtain

$$\cos \alpha \sin \beta \equiv \tfrac{1}{2}[\sin(\alpha + \beta) - \sin(\alpha - \beta)]. \qquad (6\text{–}24)$$

Similarly, using (6–10), by adding and then subtracting, we obtain

$$\cos \alpha \cos \beta \equiv \tfrac{1}{2}[\cos(\alpha + \beta) + \cos(\alpha - \beta)], \qquad (6\text{–}25)$$

$$\sin \alpha \sin \beta \equiv \tfrac{1}{2}[\cos(\alpha - \beta) - \cos(\alpha + \beta)]. \qquad (6\text{–}26)$$

As an example, the product $\cos 6\theta \cos 3\theta$ may be represented as a sum. Using (6–25) with $\alpha = 6\theta$ and $\beta = 3\theta$, we have

$$\cos 6\theta \cos 3\theta \equiv \tfrac{1}{2}(\cos 9\theta + \cos 3\theta).$$

The same four identities can also be used for transforming a sum into a product. Such a transformation is useful when logarithms are to be used, for products are more readily calculated by logarithms than are sums. For convenience, we change the notation by letting $\alpha + \beta = \theta$, and $\alpha - \beta = \omega$. Solving these equations for α and β, we obtain $\alpha = (\theta + \omega)/2$, and $\beta = (\theta - \omega)/2$. Substituting these values in the above identities and simplifying, we obtain

$$\sin \theta + \sin \omega \equiv 2 \sin \frac{\theta + \omega}{2} \cos \frac{\theta - \omega}{2}, \qquad (6\text{–}27)$$

$$\sin \theta - \sin \omega \equiv 2 \cos \frac{\theta + \omega}{2} \sin \frac{\theta - \omega}{2}, \qquad (6\text{–}28)$$

$$\cos \theta + \cos \omega \equiv 2 \cos \frac{\theta + \omega}{2} \cos \frac{\theta - \omega}{2}, \qquad (6\text{–}29)$$

$$\cos \theta - \cos \omega \equiv -2 \sin \frac{\theta + \omega}{2} \sin \frac{\theta - \omega}{2}. \qquad (6\text{–}30)$$

EXAMPLE. Express $\sin \theta + \sin 3\theta + \sin 5\theta + \sin 7\theta$ as a product.

Solution. By grouping the first two and last two terms, and using (6–27),

$$\sin \theta + \sin 3\theta + \sin 5\theta + \sin 7\theta \equiv 2 \sin \frac{\theta + 3\theta}{2} \cos \frac{\theta - 3\theta}{2} +$$

$$2 \sin \frac{5\theta + 7\theta}{2} \cos \frac{5\theta - 7\theta}{2}$$

$$\equiv 2 \sin 2\theta \cos(-\theta) + 2 \sin 6\theta \cos (-\theta)$$

$$\equiv 2 \cos \theta (\sin 2\theta + \sin 6\theta) \ (\text{Why?})$$

$$\equiv 2 \cos \theta (2 \sin 4\theta \cos 2\theta) \ (\text{Why?})$$

$$\equiv 4 \cos \theta \cos 2\theta \sin 4\theta.$$

PROBLEMS

Express each of the following products as a sum.

1. $\sin 3\theta \cos 5\theta$
2. $4 \cos \pi/3 \cos \pi/6$
3. $\cos 7\theta \sin 5\theta$
4. $6 \sin 2\pi/3 \sin \pi/3$
5. $\sin 5\theta \cos 2\theta$
6. $\cos 2\theta \cos 6\theta$
7. $\cos \theta \sin \theta/2$
8. $2 \sin 7\theta \sin 2\theta$

Express each of the following sums as products.

9. $\sin \pi/9 + \sin 2\pi/9$
10. $\cos 2\theta - \cos \theta$
11. $\cos 7\pi/9 + \cos 2\pi/9$
12. $\sin \pi/4 - \sin \pi/5$
13. $\sin 8\theta + \sin 4\theta$
14. $\cos 4\theta - \cos 8\theta$
15. $\sin 5\theta/3 - \sin 5\theta/6$
16. $\cos 6\theta + \cos 7\theta$

Prove the following identities:

17. $\dfrac{\sin 5\theta - \sin 3\theta}{\cos 5\theta + \cos 3\theta} \equiv \tan \theta$

18. $\dfrac{\cos 6\theta + \cos 4\theta}{\sin 6\theta - \sin 4\theta} \equiv \cot \theta$

19. $\dfrac{\sin 8\theta + \sin 2\theta}{\cos 8\theta + \cos 2\theta} \equiv \tan 5\theta$

20. $\dfrac{\sin 3\theta - \sin \theta}{\cos^2 \theta - \sin^2 \theta} \equiv 2 \sin \theta$

21. $\dfrac{\sin \alpha - \sin \beta}{\cos \alpha + \cos \beta} \equiv \tan \dfrac{\alpha - \beta}{2}$

22. $\dfrac{\sin \alpha - \sin \beta}{\sin \alpha + \sin \beta} \equiv \dfrac{\tan \frac{1}{2}(\alpha - \beta)}{\tan \frac{1}{2}(\alpha + \beta)}$

23. $\dfrac{\sin \theta + \sin 3\theta + \sin 5\theta}{\cos \theta + \cos 3\theta + \cos 5\theta} \equiv \tan 3\theta$

24. $\sin \left(\dfrac{\pi}{4} - \theta\right) \sin \left(\dfrac{\pi}{4} + \theta\right) \equiv \frac{1}{2} \cos 2\theta$

6-4 Circular function equations. The second type of equation in mathematics is the *conditional equation*. Such an equation does *not* hold true for all permissible values of the quantities involved. One is usually required to solve such an equation, or to find all possible values (the solution) for which the equation is true.

EXAMPLE 1. $3x - 12 = 0$ is true for only the one value $x = 4$.

EXAMPLE 2. $x^2 - 7x + 10 = 0$ is true for only two values, $x = 2$ and 5.

EXAMPLE 3. $\sin \theta = \cos \theta$ is true for only two values between 0 and 2π, $\theta = \pi/4$ and $5\pi/4$.

There is no general rule for finding the solution of an equation involving circular functions, although algebraic methods as well as identities between the circular functions are used. The following suggestions will help in many cases:

(1) If only one function of a single angle is involved, it usually is possible to solve algebraically for the values of the function. From this the solution can be determined.

EXAMPLE 1. Solve the equation $4 \sin^2 \theta = 3$ for all values of θ.

Solution. Since $\sin^2 \theta = 3/4$,

$$\sin \theta = + \sqrt{3}/2 \text{ or } \sin \theta = - \sqrt{3}/2,$$

giving

$$\theta = \pi/3, \ 2\pi/3 \text{ or } \theta = 4\pi/3, \ 5\pi/3,$$

as the values between 0 and 2π. Therefore,

$$\theta = (\tfrac{1}{3} + n)\pi, \text{ or } (\tfrac{2}{3} + n)\pi$$

for any integer n.

---

(2) If one side of a given equation is zero and the other side is factorable, each factor may be set equal to zero, as in algebra, and these equations solved.

EXAMPLE 2. Find the solution of $\tan \theta \sin \theta - \tan \theta = 0$.

Solution. By factoring

$$\tan \theta \ (\sin \theta - 1) = 0,$$

and setting each factor equal to zero,

$$\tan \theta = 0, \qquad \sin \theta = 1.$$

The values of θ satisfying these relations $(0 \leqslant \theta < 2\pi)$ are

$$\theta = 0 \text{ or } \pi, \quad \text{and} \quad \theta = \pi/2.$$

Therefore, in general,

$$\theta = (0 + n)\pi, \quad \text{or} \quad (\tfrac{1}{2} + 2n)\pi.$$

---

(3) If several functions of a single angle are involved, it is frequently quite possible, by using certain identities, to express all the functions in terms of a single function.

EXAMPLE 3.   Solve $\cos^2 \theta + 5 \sin \theta + 2 = 0$.

Solution.   Since $\cos^2 \theta$ may be expressed as $1 - \sin^2 \theta$, it is possible to rewrite this equation entirely in terms of $\sin \theta$.   Thus,

$$1 - \sin^2 \theta + 5 \sin \theta + 2 = 0,$$

or

$$\sin^2 \theta - 5 \sin \theta - 3 = 0.$$

Since the left side is not factorable, the equation is most easily solved for $\sin \theta$ by making use of the formula $x = (-b \pm \sqrt{b^2 - 4ac})/2a$ for the roots of the quadratic equation $ax^2 + bx + c = 0$.   Thus,

$$\sin \theta = \frac{5 \pm \sqrt{25 + 12}}{2} = \frac{5 \pm 6.0828}{2} ,$$

or

$$\sin \theta = 5.5414, \quad \text{or} \quad -0.5414.$$

Since $|\sin \theta| \leq 1$, we consider only the value -0.5414, which results in an angle in the third quadrant and one in the fourth quadrant. Using Table I, we have

$$\theta = 180° + 32°47' \quad \text{or} \quad 360° - 32°47'.$$

Therefore, in general, using (5–1),

$$\theta = n180° - (-1)^n 32°47'.$$

EXAMPLE 4.   Solve $3 \sin \theta + 4 \cos \theta = 5$.

Solution.   In Example 5, Article 3–3, the left side of this equation was expressed as $5 \sin(\theta + \theta_1)$, where θ_1 had its sine equal to $4/5$ and its cosine equal to $3/5$.   (Also compare Example 2, Article 5–5.) Thus

$$3 \sin \theta + 4 \cos \theta = 5 \sin(\theta + 53°08' + n360°) = 5,$$

so that

$$\sin(\theta + 53°08' + n360°) = 1,$$

or

$$\theta + 53°08' = 90° + n360°.$$

Thus

$$\theta = 36°52' + n360°.$$

If, in solving the equation, each side of the equation is raised to a power, the results must be checked as in algebra, for raising to a power is not a reversible operation and extraneous roots may be introduced.   It is also important to realize that the general solution may be written in different forms.   This will be evident in checking the answers to the problems.

PROBLEMS

Solve the following equations for all values of θ.

1. $4 \sin^2 \theta = 1$

2. $4 \cos^2 \theta = 3$

3. $1 - \cos^2 \theta = \cos^2 \theta$

4. $\sin \theta = \cos \theta$

5. $\tan^2 \theta = 3$

6. $\tan \theta (2 \sin \theta - \sqrt{3}) = 0$

7. $\cot \theta (2 \cos \theta - 1) = 0$

8. $\cot^2 \theta - \cot \theta = 0$

9. $2 \tan^2 \theta + \tan \theta = 0$

10. $\cos^2 \theta - 3 \cos \theta = 0$

11. $2 \sin^2 \theta - \sin \theta = 1$

12. $2 \cos^2 \theta + 3 \cos \theta + 1 = 0$

13. $\tan^2 \theta + \tan \theta + 1 = 0$

14. $\tan^2 \theta - 3 \sec \theta + 3 = 0$

15. $2 \cos^2 \theta + 3 \sin \theta = 0$

16. $4 \sin^2 \theta - \cos \theta - 2 = 0$

17. $3 \sec^2 \theta + \tan \theta - 5 = 0$

18. $\cot 2\theta = 2 + \tan 2\theta$

19. $4 \sin^2 2\theta + 2 \cos 2\theta = 3$

20. $\tan 2\theta + 5 = 3 \sec^2 2\theta$

21. $2 \sin 3\theta \cos 3\theta = -1$

22. $\sin 2\theta = \cos \theta$

23. $\cos 2\theta = \sin \theta$

24. $\sin \theta \cos 2\theta + \cos \theta \sin 2\theta = 1$

25. $\cos 3\theta \cos \theta + \sin 3\theta \sin \theta = -1$

26. $\sin \left(\theta + \dfrac{\pi}{6} \right) = \cos \left(\theta + \dfrac{\pi}{6} \right)$

27. $\tan \left(\theta + \dfrac{\pi}{4} \right) - \tan \left(\theta - \dfrac{\pi}{4} \right) = 4$

28. $4 \sin \theta + 3 \cos \theta = 2$

29. $\cos \theta - 2 = \sqrt{3} \sin \theta$

30. $12 \cos \theta - 5 \sin \theta = 13$

31. $\sin \theta + \cos \theta = 1$

32. $\left(\theta - \dfrac{\pi}{2} \right)(\sin \theta + 1) = 0$

33. $(\theta - 3)(\cos \theta - 2) = 0$

34. $(\theta + \pi)(\tan \theta - 2) = 0$

35. $\sin \theta \cos \theta - 2 \cos \theta - 3 \sin \theta + 6 = 0$

CHAPTER 7

COMPLEX NUMBERS

The possibility of extensions or generalizations of the real number system was mentioned in Chapter 1. One of these is a most useful algebra of all ordered pairs of real numbers, which we shall discuss briefly. The most common interpretation of this algebra will then be considered in some detail.

7-1 Algebra of ordered pairs. With the set of all ordered pairs of numbers (x,y) as elements, where x and y are real numbers, we can set up an algebra. We shall define two ordered pairs (x_1,y_1) and (x_2,y_2) to be *equal** if and only if $x_1 = x_2$ and $y_1 = y_2$. Thus, $(x + 2y, 2x - y) = (4,3)$ if and only if $x + 2y = 4$ and $2x - y = 3$ or, specifically, $x = 2$ and $y = 1$.

We next define the fundamental operations of addition, subtraction, multiplication, and division. The *sum* of two ordered pairs (x_1,y_1) and (x_2,y_2) is here defined as the ordered pair $(x_1 + x_2, y_1 + y_2)$ and is written

$$(x_1,y_1) + (x_2,y_2) = (x_1 + x_2, y_1 + y_2). \qquad (7\text{-}1)$$

As in the case of real numbers, where the solution for x of the equation $a + x = b$, written $b - a$, is called the difference, the solution for (x,y) in the equation

$$(x_1,y_1) + (x,y) = (x_2,y_2)\dagger \qquad (7\text{-}2)$$

is called the *difference* of the two ordered pairs (x_2,y_2) and (x_1,y_1). Since (7-2) implies

$$x_1 + x = x_2, \qquad y_1 + y = y_2,$$

or

$$x = x_2 - x_1, \qquad y = y_2 - y_1,$$

the difference (x,y) is written as the ordered pair, $(x_2 - x_1, y_2 - y_1)$, or

---

* These definitions of equality, addition, and multiplication are by no means the only possible ones for ordered pairs, but have been chosen specifically for the introduction of the complex number system.

† Equations (7-2) and (7-5) have unique solutions for (x,y).

$$(x_2,y_2) - (x_1,y_1) = (x_2 - x_1, y_2 - y_1). \qquad (7\text{–}3)$$

The definition of multiplication is not as obvious as that of addition. We define the *product* of two ordered pairs by the equation

$$(x_1,y_1) \cdot (x_2,y_2) = (x_1 x_2 - y_1 y_2, x_1 y_2 + x_2 y_1). \qquad (7\text{–}4)$$

For example,

$$(2,1) \cdot (3,2) = (2 \cdot 3 - 1 \cdot 2, 2 \cdot 2 + 3 \cdot 1) = (4,7).$$

Again, as in the case of real numbers, where division is defined in terms of multiplication, the definition for the quotient of two ordered pairs follows the same pattern. Since the real number $x = a/b$ is defined by the equation $bx = a$, we define as the *quotient* of two ordered pairs, the ordered pair, (x,y), which is the solution of the equation

$$(x_2,y_2) \cdot (x,y) = (x_1,y_1);^* \qquad (x_2,y_2) \neq (0,0). \qquad (7\text{–}5)$$

Using (7–4), this becomes

$$(xx_2 - yy_2, xy_2 + x_2y) = (x_1,y_1),$$

and, therefore,

$$x_2 x - y_2 y = x_1, \qquad y_2 x + x_2 y = y_1.$$

Solving for x and y, we get the solution

$$x = \frac{x_1 x_2 + y_1 y_2}{x_2{}^2 + y_2{}^2},$$

$$y = \frac{x_2 y_1 - x_1 y_2}{x_2{}^2 + y_2{}^2}.$$

Thus the quotient of two ordered pairs may be written

$$\frac{(x_1,y_1)}{(x_2,y_2)} = \left(\frac{x_1 x_2 + y_1 y_2}{x_2{}^2 + y_2{}^2}, \frac{x_2 y_1 - x_1 y_2}{x_2{}^2 + y_2{}^2} \right). \qquad (7\text{–}6)$$

For example,

$$\frac{(4,8)}{(3,1)} = (2,2).$$

It can easily be verified that the elements of this algebra of ordered pairs satisfy the laws (1–1) stated in Chapter 1.

---

* Equations (7–2) and (7–5) have unique solutions for (x,y).

7-2 Complex numbers. One of the most common interpretations of the algebra of ordered pairs, discussed in Article 7-1, is the algebra of complex numbers. The symbol $x + yi$, where x and y are real numbers and i has the property that $i^2 = -1$, is called a *complex number*. If $y = 0$, of course the complex number is real; if $y \neq 0$, the complex number is said to be *imaginary*. With $y \neq 0$, and $x = 0$, $x + yi$ is a *pure imaginary*.

We notice immediately, with the numbers x and y obeying the ordinary laws for real numbers, and the new element i obeying the law

$$i^2 = -1,$$

that the complex numbers $x + yi$ may be thought of as an abbreviation for the ordered pairs, since $x + yi$ satisfies the same operations as the ordered pairs (x,y). Specifically, in considering the sum of two complex numbers,

$$(x_1 + y_1 i) + (x_2 + y_2 i) = (x_1 + x_2) + (y_1 + y_2)i. \qquad (7-7)$$

With regard to the product of two complex numbers,

$$(x_1 + y_1 i) \cdot (x_2 + y_2 i) = x_1 x_2 + x_1 y_2 i + x_2 y_1 i + y_1 y_2 i^2$$
$$= (x_1 x_2 - y_1 y_2) + (x_1 y_2 + x_2 y_1)i. \qquad (7-8)$$

We see in this equation the real reason for defining the product of two ordered pairs as given by (7-4). The quotient of two complex numbers is given by

$$\frac{x_1 + y_1 i}{x_2 + y_2 i} = \frac{(x_1 + y_1 i)(x_2 - y_2 i)}{(x_2 + y_2 i)(x_2 - y_2 i)}$$
$$= \frac{x_1 x_2 - x_1 y_2 i + x_2 y_1 i - y_1 y_2 i^2}{x_2^2 - x_2 y_2 i + x_2 y_2 i - y_2^2 i^2}$$
$$= \frac{x_1 x_2 + y_1 y_2}{x_2^2 + y_2^2} + \frac{x_2 y_1 - x_1 y_2}{x_2^2 + y_2^2}\, i. \qquad (7-9)$$

Thus, the ordered pair (x,y) may be considered as representing the complex number $x + yi$.

Two complex numbers which differ only in the sign of their imaginary parts are called *conjugates* of each other. Thus, $3 + 2i$ and $3 - 2i$ or $5i$ and $-5i$ are conjugate complex numbers. In general, $x + yi$ and $x - yi$ are numbers of this type. Note Problems 24 and 25.

It is unfortunate that the word imaginary has been applied to these numbers. Although they were originally introduced to solve quadratic equations, they have been extremely useful in physics and engineering, especially in the description of certain electrical phenomena. In such situations, the "imaginary numbers" have significance which is quite as real as that of the "real" numbers.

PROBLEMS

In this algebra defined for ordered pairs, show

1. $(x,y) \cdot (0,0) = (0,0)$
2. $(x,y) + (0,0) = (x,y)$
3. $(x,y) \cdot (1,0) = (x,y)$
4. $(x,y) = (y,x)$ if and only if $x = y$
5. $(0,1)^2 = (0,1) \cdot (0,1) = (-1,0)$

6. What ordered pair in this algebra of ordered pairs takes the place of zero in our ordinary number system? What ordered pair takes the place of one?

Find the value of (x,y) in Problems 7 through 15.

7. $(x,y) = (2,3) + (4,5)$
8. $(x,y) = (-2,1) + (3,-7)$
9. $(x,y) = (3,-1) - (4,-2)$
10. $(3,1) = (x,y) + (5,-1)$
11. $(x,y) = (3,1) \cdot (2,3)$
12. $(x,y) = (-1,2) \cdot (3,-5)$
13. $(x,y) = (2,-1)/(-1,3)$
14. $(x,y) = (23,11)/(5,-1)$
15. $(x,y) = \left(-\dfrac{1}{2}, \dfrac{\sqrt{3}}{2}\right)^3$

In Problems 16 through 19, give the expression as a single complex number.

16. (a) $(2 + 5i) + (4 - i)$,   (b) $(2 + 5i) - (4 - i)$
17. (a) $(2 + 5i)(4 - i)$,   (b) $(2 + 5i)(4 + i)$
18. (a) $\dfrac{2 + 5i}{4 - i}$,   (b) $\dfrac{2 + 5i}{4 + i}$
19. (a) $i^3 = i \cdot i^2$ (b) $i^4 = i^2 \cdot i^2$ (c) i^5 (d) $1/i$

20. Prove, for any positive integer n,

(a) $i^{4n} = 1$ (b) $i^{4n+1} = i$ (c) $i^{4n+2} = -1$ (d) $i^{4n+3} = -i$

(e) $i^{n+4} = i^n$.

In the following problems, use the ordinary properties of the real numbers, and the fact that $i^2 = -1$.

21. State Problems 7, 11, and 13, interpreting the ordered pairs as numbers, and solve.

22. If the complex number $x + yi = 0$, show algebraically that $x = 0$ and $y = 0$. *Hint:* Since $x = -yi$, $x^2 = -y^2$. What can be said about x and y?

23. If $x_1 + y_1 i$ and $x_2 + y_2 i$ are two complex numbers such that $x_1 + y_1 i = x_2 + y_2 i$, show by using algebra that $x_1 = x_2$ and $y_1 = y_2$. *Hint:* By transposing, $x_1 - x_2 + (y_1 - y_2)i = 0$. Then use Problem 22.

24. Prove that the sum and product of two conjugate complex numbers are both real.

25. Prove that if the sum and product of two imaginary numbers are real, the numbers are conjugate complex numbers.

7-3 Graphical representation of complex numbers. The interpretation of the ordered pair (x,y) as the complex number $x + yi$ lends itself to a simple graphical representation of the complex numbers. Since (x,y) may be plotted as a point in the rectangular coordinate system, every complex number $x + yi$ may be associated with some point in the plane, and every point in the plane with some complex number. This plane is called the *complex plane*, and the figure on which the complex numbers are plotted is called the *Argand diagram*.* The real numbers lie on the x-axis, the pure imaginaries on the y-axis, and a number such as $5 - 2i$ is represented by the point $(5, -2)$.

Any point $P(x,y)$ in the plane, other than $(0,0)$, lies on some circle with center at $(0,0)$, whose radius is r, where $r = \sqrt{x^2 + y^2}$. Let θ be the angle in standard position having OP as its terminal side (see Fig. 7-1), so that

$$x = r \cos \theta, \qquad y = r \sin \theta. \qquad (7\text{-}10)$$

---

* The system of representing complex numbers graphically was discovered independently by Wessel (Norwegian), Argand (French), and Gauss (German) about 1800.

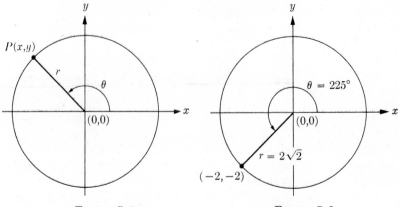

FIGURE 7–1   FIGURE 7–2

Thus the complex number, $x + yi$, may be written in *trigonometric form*,

$$x + yi = r (\cos \theta + i \sin \theta).* \qquad (7\text{--}11)$$

Since $\sin \theta$ and $\cos \theta$ are both periodic with period $2\pi = 360°$, for $r > 0$ and any integer k,

$$r \cos (\theta + k360°) + i \sin (\theta + k360°)$$

is also a trigonometric form for $x + yi$. We note that r must be greater than zero. This value of

$$r = \sqrt{x^2 + y^2} \qquad (7\text{--}12)$$

is called the *absolute value* or *modulus* of $x + yi$. The angle θ is called the *amplitude* or *argument* of $x + yi$.

EXAMPLE 1. Express the complex number $-2 - 2i$ in trigonometric form.

Solution. By locating the point $(-2, -2)$ which corresponds to $-2 - 2i$ (see Fig. 7–2), we have

$$r = \sqrt{(-2)^2 + (-2)^2} = 2\sqrt{2}$$

and $\tan \theta = 1$, with θ terminating in the third quadrant. Thus,

$$\theta = 225°,$$

---

* This form, $r(\cos + i \sin \theta)$, is sometimes abbreviated $r \operatorname{cis} \theta$.

and $-2 - 2i = 2\sqrt{2} \, (\cos 225° + i \sin 225°).$

EXAMPLE 2.   Express the complex number $3 \, (\cos 150° + i \sin 150°)$ in the form $x + yi$.

Solution.   On the terminal side of the angle of 150° in standard position, locate the point P, 3 units from the origin, as in Fig. 7-3. Since $P(x,y)$ represents the complex number, we have

$$x = 3 \cos 150° = -3\sqrt{3}/2,$$

and

$$y = 3 \sin 150° = 3/2.$$

Hence,

$$3 \, (\cos 150° + i \sin 150°) = -\frac{3\sqrt{3}}{2} + \frac{3}{2} i.$$

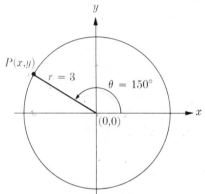

FIGURE 7-3

One of the advantages of the trigonometric form for complex numbers is its usefulness in obtaining products. By letting $r_1 \, (\cos \theta_1 + i \sin \theta_1)$ and $r_2 \, (\cos \theta_2 + i \sin \theta_2)$ be two complex numbers, we find

$$r_1 \, (\cos \theta_1 + i \sin \theta_1) \cdot r_2 \, (\cos \theta_2 + i \sin \theta_2)$$

$$= r_1 r_2 \, (\cos \theta_1 \cos \theta_2 + i \cos \theta_1 \sin \theta_2 + i \sin \theta_1 \cos \theta_2 + i^2 \sin \theta_1 \sin \theta_2)$$

$$= r_1 r_2 \, [(\cos \theta_1 \cos \theta_2 - \sin \theta_1 \sin \theta_2) + i \, (\sin \theta_1 \cos \theta_2 + \cos \theta_1 \sin \theta_2)]$$

$$= r_1 r_2 \, [\cos \, (\theta_1 + \theta_2) + i \sin \, (\theta_1 + \theta_2)]. \tag{7-13}$$

Thus, the modulus of the product of two complex numbers is the product of the moduli, and the amplitude is the sum of the amplitudes.

PROBLEMS

1. Locate the point representing graphically each of the following complex numbers. Give the trigonometric form for each, using the least positive or zero value of its amplitude.

(a) 2

(b) -2

(c) $3i$

(d) $-i$

(e) $2 - 2i$

(f) $-2 + 2i$

(g) $-\dfrac{1}{2} + \dfrac{\sqrt{3}}{2}\,i$

(h) $-\dfrac{1}{2} - \dfrac{\sqrt{3}}{2}\,i$

2. Express each of the following in the form $x + yi$.

(a) $3(\cos 0° + i \sin 0°)$

(b) $2(\cos 90° + i \sin 90°)$

(c) $\cos 180° + i \sin 180°$

(d) $2(\cos 225° + i \sin 225°)$

(e) $2(\cos 270° + i \sin 270°)$

(f) $8(\cos 135° + i \sin 135°)$

(g) $4(\cos 300° + i \sin 300°)$

(h) $6(\cos 150° + i \sin 150°)$

3. Perform the multiplications, expressing the final result in the form $x + yi$. Check your result by expressing each of the given numbers in the form $x + yi$, and then performing the multiplication algebraically.

(a) $3(\cos 60° + i \sin 60°) \cdot 2(\cos 30° + i \sin 30°)$

(b) $4(\cos 120° + i \sin 120°) \cdot 2(\cos 90° + i \sin 90°)$

(c) $3(\cos 135° + i \sin 135°) \cdot 4(\cos (-45°) + i \sin (-45°))$

(d) $[2(\cos 120° + i \sin 120°)]^3$

4. Prove that the quotient of the two complex numbers $r_1(\cos \theta_1 + i \sin \theta_1)$ and $r_2(\cos \theta_2 + i \sin \theta_2)$ is given by

$$\frac{r_1}{r_2}[\cos (\theta_1 - \theta_2) + i \sin (\theta_1 - \theta_2)]. \qquad (7\text{--}14)$$

5. Use (7–14) to perform the following divisions. Check as in Problem 3.

(a) $4(\cos 60° + i \sin 60°) \div 2(\cos 30° + i \sin 30°)$

(b) $6(\cos 0° + i \sin 0°) \div 3(\cos 240° + i \sin 240°)$

6. Prove that the reciprocal of $r(\cos \theta + i \sin \theta)$ is

$$\frac{1}{r}(\cos \theta - i \sin \theta).$$

7. Prove that $[r(\cos \theta + i \sin \theta)]^2 = r^2(\cos 2\theta + i \sin 2\theta)$.

8. In considering formula (7–10), we recall a similar formula, (4–14), given in Chapter 4. These are indeed the same, if in the ordered pairs considered in this chapter the x and y are thought of as representing the x- and y-components of a vector from the origin to the point (x,y). More specifically, this algebra of ordered pairs may be interpreted as a study of vectors in the plane. By plotting the following number pairs with their sum and

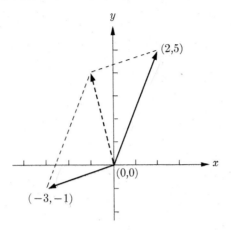

FIGURE 7-4

drawing the appropriate vectors, show that the parallelogram law for the sum of two vectors is satisfied (see Problem 22, Article 4-4).

(a) $(2,5) + (-3,-1) =$ (b) $(-1,2) + (4,-5) =$

Hint: See Fig. 7-4.

(c) $(3,-2) + (-2,3) =$ (d) $(-3,-2) + (6,4) =$

7-4 Powers and roots of complex numbers. In Article 7-3, we obtained an expression for the product of two complex numbers in trigonometric form. By using (7-13), we immediately have

$$[r.(\cos \theta + i \sin \theta)]^2 = r^2 (\cos 2\theta + i \sin 2\theta),$$

or

$$[r (\cos \theta + i \sin \theta)]^3 = r^3 (\cos 3\theta + i \sin 3\theta).$$

In fact, we can prove by mathematical induction* a general theorem.

THEOREM.   If n is any positive integer,

$$[r (\cos \theta + i \sin \theta)]^n = r^n (\cos n\theta + i \sin n\theta).   (7-15)$$

This theorem holds for rational, irrational and even complex values of the exponent, but we shall make use of it only with integral values.

---

* This result, known as De Moivre's Theorem, was discovered by Abraham De Moivre (1667-1754). For students who understand mathematical induction, the proof, where n is an integer, is immediate. Obviously, it is true when $n = 1$. We must merely show that the statement for $n = k$ implies the statement for $n = k + 1$.

EXAMPLE 1.   Show that $z^3 = 1$ if $z = -1/2 + (\sqrt{3}/2)i$.

Solution.   Putting z in trigonometric form, we have

$$z = \cos 120° + i \sin 120°.$$
Thus,
$$z^3 = (\cos 120° + i \sin 120°)^3$$
$$= \cos 3(120°) + i \sin 3(120°)$$
$$= \cos 360° + i \sin 360° = 1.$$

A more important use of (7–15) is made in finding the roots of complex numbers. In our discussion we should recall that for r positive, the notation $\sqrt[n]{r}$ represents the principal nth root of r, that is, the only nth root of r which is positive and real.

EXAMPLE 2.   Find the three cube roots of $-2 - 2\sqrt{3}i$.

Solution. Expressing our answer in trigonometric form, $r(\cos \theta + i \sin \theta)$, we are seeking values of r and θ such that

$$[r(\cos \theta + i \sin \theta)]^3 = -2 - 2\sqrt{3}i,$$

or, also expressing $-2 - 2\sqrt{3}i$ in trigonometric form,

$$r^3(\cos 3\theta + i \sin 3\theta) = 16(\cos 240° + i \sin 240°).$$

When two complex numbers are equal, their moduli are equal, and their amplitudes are either equal or differ by integral multiples of 360°. Thus,
$$r^3 = 16, \quad \text{and} \quad 3\theta = 240° + k360°,$$
or
$$r = 2\sqrt[3]{2}, \qquad \theta = 80° + k120°,$$

where k is any positive or negative integer, or zero. Hence $r(\cos \theta + i \sin \theta)$ will be

$$2\sqrt[3]{2}(\cos 80° + i \sin 80°), \quad \text{for } k = 0,$$
$$2\sqrt[3]{2}(\cos 200° + i \sin 200°), \quad \text{for } k = 1,$$
$$2\sqrt[3]{2}(\cos 320° + i \sin 320°), \quad \text{for } k = 2.$$

These three values are all distinct, and represent the three different cube roots of $-2 - 2\sqrt{3}i$. For any other integral value of k, the expression will reduce to one of these three, so that these three numbers are the only cube roots. A complex number has three and only three cube roots, four and only four fourth roots, and, in general, n and only n nth roots. Should it be required to reduce our answers to the form $x + yi$, we can use tables to find $2\sqrt[3]{2}$ and the values of the functions of 80°, 200°, and 320°.

The general theorem concerning such roots should now be apparent.

THEOREM.   For any complex number $r\,(\cos\theta + i\sin\theta)$ and any positive integer n,

$$\sqrt[n]{r}\,(\cos\theta_k + i\sin\theta_k), \qquad (7\text{–}16)$$

where

$$\theta_k = \frac{\theta + k360°}{n}, \quad k = 0,1,2,\cdots(n-1),$$

represents the n distinct nth roots of $r\,(\cos\theta + i\sin\theta)$.

Proof.   To show that (7–16) is an nth root of $r\,(\cos\theta + i\sin\theta)$ for each k, we merely use (7–15) to raise it to the nth power:

$$[\sqrt[n]{r}\,(\cos\theta_k + i\sin\theta_k)]^n = r\,(\cos n\theta_k + i\sin n\theta_k)$$
$$= r\,[\cos(\theta + k360°) + i\sin(\theta + k360°)]$$
$$= r\,(\cos\theta + i\sin\theta).$$

Also we must notice that the n complex numbers given by (7–16) for the n different values of k are distinct, since no two of their amplitudes differ by a multiple of 360°.

The use of formula (7–16) will enable us to find the n nth roots of any complex number directly by substitution.

PROBLEMS

Write each of the expressions in Problems 1–7 in the form $x + yi$.

1. $[2\,(\cos 15° + i\sin 15°)]^6$
2. $[3\,(\cos 120° + i\sin 120°)]^5$
3. $[2\,(\cos 315° + i\sin 315°)]^3$
4. $(\cos 36° + i\sin 36°)^{10}$
5. $\left(-\dfrac{\sqrt{3}}{2} + \dfrac{i}{2}\right)^5$
6. $(1 - i)^8$
7. $\left(\dfrac{1}{\sqrt{2}} + \dfrac{i}{\sqrt{2}}\right)^{200}$

Find and represent graphically Problems 8–15.

8. The square roots of $4 + 4\sqrt{3}i$

9. The square roots of $-16i$

10. The cube roots of 1

11. The cube roots of -8

12. The fourth roots of $4 - 4\sqrt{3}i$

13. The fourth roots of $16 (\cos 120° + i \sin 120°)$

14. The cube roots of $8 (\cos 300° + i \sin 300°)$

15. The tenth roots of 1.   Compare the figure with Fig. 2–17.

Solve the equations in Problems 16–19, expressing the roots in the form $x + yi$, and represent them graphically.

16. $z^6 = 64$ 17. $z^4 = 1$

18. $z^3 + i = 0$ 19. $z^5 + 32 = 0$

CHAPTER 8

APPLICATIONS OF THE CIRCULAR FUNCTION TO PERIODIC PHENOMENA

A large number of the problems with which science deals today are periodic in nature. Such problems are found in astronomy and mechanics, and in dealing with the phenomena of light, sound, and electricity. The analysis of these problems requires, among other things, the frequent use of the circular functions, with special emphasis on certain of their properties.

The notion of simple harmonic motion is fundamental to any discussion of periodic phenomena. Examples of bodies which move approximately according to the laws of such motion are the bob of a simple pendulum, the bobbing up and down of a floating cork, a particle in a vibrating violin string, a point on the prong of a tuning fork, a particle of air during the passage of a sound wave, or a particle of earth during a small earthquake. Simple harmonic motion will be discussed in addition to other applications of the graph of $y = a \sin (kx + b)$.

8–1 Simple harmonic motion. Actually, any body whose position d on a straight line is given at any instant t by the equation $d = a \sin \omega t$ is said to describe *simple harmonic motion*. Because of this definition, we need only to recall the properties of this function to recognize some of the evident features of simple harmonic motion. The motion is oscillatory in character, repeating itself in definite intervals of time. Thus, it is periodic. The *amplitude* of the motion is the magnitude of the maximum value of $a \sin \omega t$, or a; that is, the magnitude of the displacement from the central point of the motion. The time required for one complete vibration is called the *period* $(2\pi/\omega)$. The term *cycle* is used in place of vibration, in connection with electric current. The number of complete periods per unit time, namely, $1/(2\pi/\omega)$ or $\omega/2\pi$, is called the *frequency* of the simple harmonic motion. The *phase* at any instant is the fractional part of the period which has elapsed since the body passed through its central position in the positive direction. Actually, the position of the body need not be given from the time when $t = 0$, but may be

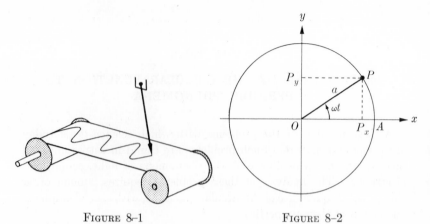

FIGURE 8–1   FIGURE 8–2

given from any time t_0. Thus the more general equation may be written $d = a \sin \omega(t - t_0)$. We have learned that this more general equation represents the same curve, except for a shift along the t-axis. This equation also describes simple harmonic motion, for it can be written $d = a \sin \omega t'$, where $t' = t - t_0$. Since $y = a \sin kt$ and $y = a \cos kt$ differ only in phase, $d = a \cos \omega t$ also is used to describe simple harmonic motion.

It is interesting to observe that a graph of a simple harmonic motion can be obtained directly from a demonstration of such a motion. This is illustrated by considering the swinging of a simple pendulum from a fixed point, and the marking of its trace on a sheet of paper moving at a constant velocity. From Fig. 8–1 it should be clear that the displacement of the bob from its central position is a function of the time.

One of the simplest examples of a simple harmonic motion is produced by a point moving at a uniform velocity around the circumference of a circle. Consider the circle with center at O and a radius a in Fig. 8–2. If the point P is thought of as moving with constant or uniform velocity on the circle, the question arises as to the type of motion of the point P_x or P_y, that is, the projection of P on the x-axis or the projection of P on the y-axis. Suppose the constant angular velocity of P is ω radians per second,* and the point P starts at A. Then the measure of the angle traveled by P in

* It is left as an exercise to distinguish between angular velocity expressed in radians per second, and linear velocity expressed in linear units per second. *Hint:* Recall $s = r\theta$.

any time t, expressed in seconds, is ωt; thus P_y moves so that its y-coordinate is given by $y = a \sin \omega t$, and the projection of P on the y-axis describes simple harmonic motion. It is interesting to notice that P_y is at the origin when $t = 0$ and, as P_y moves up, its velocity decreases until it is 0 at C. The point P_y then moves down, increasing in velocity until it attains its maximum as it passes through O, diminishing again in velocity until it becomes 0 at C'; it then moves up with increasing velocity to its starting point O. Then the whole motion is repeated. Actually, the velocity of any body describing simple harmonic motion increases and decreases as it does in this case.

PROBLEMS

1. What can be said about the motion of the point P_x in Fig. 8–2? Obtain an expression of its position at any time t.

2. The following equations represent simple harmonic motions. Give their amplitudes, their periods, their frequencies, and sketch their graphs.

(a) $y = 8 \sin 2x$ (b) $y = 10 \sin (t/3)$

(c) $y = \frac{1}{4} \sin 3t$ (d) $y = 7 \cos 5x$

(e) $y = 4 \sin 2\pi x$ (f) $y = a \sin \omega t$

3. A particle moves along a line in such a way that its displacement from a fixed point of the line is given by $d = 2 \sin^2 t$. Can this motion be expressed as simple harmonic motion? What is its period? *Hint:* Can $\cos 2\theta$ be expressed in terms of $\sin^2 \theta$?

4. The quantity of electric current is measured in amperes, a unit denoting the number of electrons which pass a fixed point in a wire during one second. With a simple generator this quantity of current is expressed by

$$I = a_1 \sin \omega t.$$

Give the expression for I if the amplitude is 10 and the current is 60-cycle. Sketch the graph of this expression. The 60-cycle current is the frequency in common use at the present time in this country, and represents 60 cycles per second.

5. The flow of electricity also exerts a force called *electromotive force*. The expression for the electromotive force for a simplified generator is given by

$$E = a_2 \sin \omega t,$$

where the unit of measure is the volt. How can E be expressed in terms of t if its amplitude is 8 and the current is 60-cycle?

6. The amount of power of an electrical current to light lamps, generate heat, or operate machinery is dependent on its energy at any time t. This electrical energy or power is usually expressed in kilowatt hours, and is given

by the expression, $P = EI$. For the 60-cycle current mentioned in Problems 4 and 5, show that P can be written in the form

$$P = a_1 a_2 \sin^2 \omega t.$$

Find the period of this periodic function. Notice that P, E, and I, in Problems 4, 5, and 6, are all examples of *simple harmonic behavior*.

7. If a flute is played softly in the middle register, the sound which is produced closely approximates a simple sound. A *simple sound* is defined as one which produces on the oscillograph a wave which may be represented by a simple harmonic curve, that is, by $y = a \sin \omega t$. Give the expression and draw the graph of the equation representing such a sound if its frequency is 400 and its amplitude is 0.001 inch.

8. The pressure in a traveling sound wave is given by

$$p = 10 \sin 200\pi \ (t - x/1000) \text{ dynes cm}^2,$$

where t is in seconds and x in centimeters. Sketch p as a function of x at the following definite times: $t = 0$, $1/400$, $2/400$, $3/400$, and $4/400$ sec.

9. The equation of a traveling transverse wave in a certain chord is given by the expression

$$y = 25 \sin \pi \ (0.20t - 0.01x),$$

where x is in centimeters and t is in seconds. Graph this equation when $x = 10$, 25, and 100 cm.

8–2 Addition of two general sine functions of the same period. Any two general sine functions of the same period are represented by

$$y_1 = a \sin (\omega t + \alpha), \qquad (8\text{--}1)$$

and

$$y_2 = b \sin (\omega t + \beta).$$

Their amplitudes are a and b, their phase difference is $\beta - \alpha$, and their common period is $2\pi/\omega$. We shall show that the sum of these two functions of the same period is itself a sine function of that period. For

$$y = y_1 + y_2 = a \sin (\omega t + \alpha) + b \sin (\omega t + \beta)$$
$$= a \ (\sin \omega t \cos \alpha + \cos \omega t \sin \alpha) + b \ (\sin \omega t \cos \beta + \cos \omega t \sin \beta)$$
$$= A \sin \omega t + B \cos \omega t, \qquad (8\text{--}2)$$

where

$$A = a \cos \alpha + b \cos \beta,$$

and $\qquad\qquad\qquad B = a \sin \alpha + b \sin \beta.$

We recall that $A \sin \omega t + B \cos \omega t = r \sin (\omega t + \delta),$* where

$$r = \sqrt{A^2 + B^2}$$

$$= \sqrt{\begin{aligned}(a^2 \cos^2 \alpha + 2ab \cos \alpha \cos \beta + b^2 \cos^2 \beta) + \\ (a^2 \sin^2 \alpha + 2ab \sin \alpha \sin \beta + b^2 \sin^2 \beta)\end{aligned}}$$

$$= \sqrt{a^2 + b^2 + 2ab (\cos \alpha \cos \beta + \sin \alpha \sin \beta)}$$

$$= \sqrt{a^2 + b^2 + 2ab \cos(\beta - \alpha)},$$

and where

$$\sin \delta = B/r \quad \text{and} \quad \cos \delta = A/r.$$

Hence, $y = a \sin (\omega t + \alpha) + b \sin (\omega t + \beta) = r \sin (\omega t + \delta),$ where r and δ have the values just found.

We have proved an extremely important theorem:

THEOREM.   The sum of any two general sine curves of the same period, regardless of their phase, is a general sine curve with that same period.

This result may be generalized to include the sum of any finite number of general sine curves of the same period, and it is especially useful in the fields of electricity and sound, as the problems will indicate.

PROBLEMS

1. Two atmospheric waves give rise to pressure variations at a given point in space according to the equations

$$p_1 = a \sin 2\pi n t,$$

and

$$p_2 = a \sin (2\pi n t - 2\pi/3).$$

Calculate the amplitude of the resultant wave at this point in space.

2. Express $y = 4 \sin (\theta + \pi/6) + 5 \sin (\theta - \pi/3)$ in the form $r \sin (\theta + \delta).$

3. The electromotive force E (the measure of the pressure due to the flow of electricity) in a circuit is given by

$$E = 80 + 8.2 \sin \omega t + 4.8 \cos \omega t - 0.8 \sin 3\omega t + 1.2 \cos 3\omega t.$$

Express E in the form $A_0 + A_1 \sin (\omega t + \alpha_1) + A_2 \sin (3\omega t + \alpha_2),$ finding the values of $A_0, A_1, A_2, \alpha_1,$ and $\alpha_2.$

_____

* Compare Example 5, Article 3–3, and Example 2, Article 5–5.

4. Sketch the graphs of Problems 2 and 3. The graphs may be completed by the method of Article 5–6, called *composition of ordinates*, or sometimes the *principle of superposition*.

5. Moving or traveling waves are sometimes reflected from the boundaries of the bodies in which they move and thus introduce waves which travel in the opposite direction. These add to the original waves to produce the resulting wave according to the principle of superposition. Consider a column of air in which the equation of the original wave is given by

$$y_1 = a \sin 2\pi n \, (t - x/V),$$

and the equation of the reflected wave is

$$y_2 = a \sin 2\pi n \, (t + x/V).$$

The resulting wave is $y = y_1 + y_2$. Prove by using (6–27) that

$$y = 2a \sin 2\pi nt \cos 2\pi nx/V.$$

This is the equation for the so-called *standing wave*. It is thus named since at certain positions in the body in which the waves are moving, y is always 0; these values for x are the values for which $\cos 2\pi nx/V = 0$, that is,

$$\frac{2\pi nx}{V} = \pi/2, \, 3\pi/2, \, 5\pi/2, \text{ and so forth.}$$

For what values of x is $y = 0$? It is interesting to note that this resulting wave at any given time t is a simple harmonic expression in x; and at any position x, it represents a simple harmonic expression of t. In all musical instruments the sound is produced by standing waves.

8–3 Addition of two sine functions of different frequencies.
Consider the equations of two sine functions when they are in phase at $t = 0$, given by

$$y_1 = a \sin 2\pi n_1 t, \tag{8–3}$$

and

$$y_2 = a \sin 2\pi n_2 t.$$

The resulting sine function is then obtained by combining these functions, $y = y_1 + y_2$. Thus,

$$y = y_1 + y_2 = a \, (\sin 2\pi n_1 t + \sin 2\pi n_2 t),$$

and by using (6–27),

$$y = 2a \sin 2\pi \frac{n_1 + n_2}{2} t \cos 2\pi \frac{n_1 - n_2}{2} t. \tag{8–4}$$

This result does not represent an exact sine function, but it does under certain conditions approximate the sine function. If $n_1 - n_2$ is small compared with n_1 and n_2, the resulting equation may be regarded as a "sine function with a slowly varying amplitude." Let

$$n = \frac{n_1 + n_2}{2}, \qquad \gamma = \frac{n_1 - n_2}{2}.$$

Thus, γ is small compared with n and, as a result of this substitution, we have

$$y = 2a \cos 2\pi\gamma t \sin 2\pi nt. \tag{8-5}$$

Since γ is small in comparison with n, $\cos 2\pi\gamma t$ varies very slowly compared with $\sin 2\pi nt$; that is, the number of oscillations of the frequency n is large during the time it takes the cosine to go through one period. Thus the resultant curve becomes a sine curve of slowly varying amplitude. In the case of sound waves, this periodic variation of amplitude is heard as "beats." The number of beats per second is equal to the number of times the wave, $y = \sin 2\pi nt$, has a value of 1 and -1 per second. The principle of beating is used in connection with radio, television, wireless waves, telephone, and high-frequency electrical current.

EXAMPLE.   Sketch the graph of the curve $y = \sin 50\pi t + \sin 60\pi t$.

Solution.   By using (8-5), we have,

$$y = \sin 50\pi t + \sin 60\pi t$$
$$= 2 \cos 5\pi t \sin 55\pi t.$$

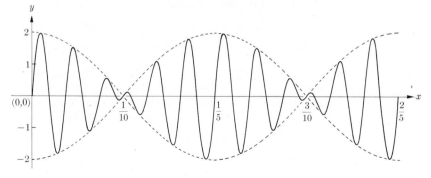

FIGURE 8-3

Since $\sin 55\pi t$ always lies between $+1$ and -1, the curve lies between the two curves $y = \pm 2 \cos 5\pi t$, touching them at the points where $\sin 55\pi t = \pm 1$. Thus it touches when $t = 1/110, 3/110, 5/110$, and so forth. The graph is shown in Fig. 8–3.

We should notice that this discussion has been for two sine functions with the same amplitudes. In the case when the amplitudes are not the same, not only is the amplitude of the resultant a varying amplitude, but also the frequency varies. Thus, any similarity of this behavior to that of a simple sine function is lost, and no discussion will be presented here.

8–4 Harmonic analysis and synthesis. A very interesting and extremely important and useful result in mathematics should be mentioned now. It can be demonstrated mathematically that any periodic piecewise continuous* curve may be approximated by a finite sum of sine and cosine curves, where the lowest frequency in the sum produces the period of the curve itself, while the remaining terms have frequencies which are integral multiples of the lowest. This method of analyzing a curve or function, known as *harmonic analysis*, was first announced by Baron J. B. J. Fourier in 1807 and first published by him in Paris in 1822. It might be expected that this method was obtained through the study of sound and wave motion but, although the result is extremely useful in such studies, the principle was discovered in the course of Fourier's study of the conduction of heat.

Fourier's Theorem may be stated in mathematical form for the periodic curve y by the approximate equality

$$y \approx a_0 + a_1 \sin \theta + a_2 \sin 2\theta + a_3 \sin 3\theta + \cdots a_n \sin n\theta$$
$$+ b_1 \cos \theta + b_2 \cos 2\theta + b_3 \cos 3\theta + \cdots b_n \cos n\theta.$$

In this expression y is the ordinate of the original curve for any particular value x, and θ, expressed in terms of x, is $2\pi x/L$. Thus, when values of x ranging from 0 to L, where L is the period of the curve, are used, it is equivalent to letting θ range from 0 to 2π. With the exception of a_0, which simply denotes the displacement of the entire

---

* Such a curve, defined on an interval of the x-axis, consists of "pieces of curves" in the intuitive sense. Any technical definition is impossible at this mathematical level.

curve from the original reference axis, each coefficient a_i and b_i is a factor indicating to what extent each individual sine or cosine curve enters into the composite. In passing, it is interesting to mention that there are machines which will obtain the expressions for all these Fourier coefficients for any curve. In other words, when a curve is given by means of a drawing, it is possible, with such a machine, to obtain the equation of this curve. These machines are called harmonic analyzers.

The converse of the analytic process which we have described is also useful. This converse process, called *harmonic synthesis*, might be described as combining several simple curves in order to obtain their resultant or composite curve. In some cases this may be accomplished by calculations. Always, although only approximately, the result may be accomplished by the graphical method suggested in Article 5–6, that of adding the measured ordinates of the individual curves and plotting the results.

8–5 Remarks on applications. Great advances have been made in the field of sound waves and especially in the study of musical sound waves by making use of harmonic analysis. The tones of the different musical instruments may be recorded, their waves produced on the oscillograph, and the results discussed mathematically. From this study, for example, the electric organ has developed.

The science *seismology*, which deals with the phenomena and origin of earthquakes, employs harmonic analysis because of the nature of its vibratory motion and resulting wave form. In the simplest case, when the vibrations are not large, the motion is essentially a simple harmonic motion; in the more general case, the wave is a composite wave. The waves are recorded by an instrument called the seismograph, and from this record the amplitude, direction of motion, and amount of periodicity of every single vibration may be computed.

Harmonic analysis and synthesis are used in predicting the tides. The United States Coast and Geodetic Survey has for one of its important functions the annual preparation and publication of a tidal calendar. This "Tide Table," issued one to two years in advance, predicts every "high and low" water at most of the principal seaports of the world. The time of the predicted occurrences is correct to the nearest minute, and the height to the nearest tenth of a foot. This is done mechanically by using the circular functions in connection with the periodic movements of the sun and moon.

Actually, applications of the circular functions in advanced astronomy are very common.

PROBLEMS

Sketch the graphs of the following curves by the method of composition of ordinates.

1. $y = \sin x + \sin \dfrac{x}{2}$

2. $y = \cos x + \cos 2x$

3. $y = 2 \sin x + 3 \sin 2x$

4. $y = 2 \left(\sin x + \frac{1}{2} \sin 2x + \frac{1}{3} \sin 3x \right)$

5. $y = \sin x + \frac{1}{3} \sin 3x + \frac{1}{5} \sin 5x$

6. $y = \dfrac{4}{\pi} \left(\sin x - \dfrac{1}{3^2} \sin 3x \right)$

By making use of the method of Article 8–3, sketch the graphs of:

7. $y = \sin 200t + \sin 210t$

8. $y = \sin 80t + \sin 100t$

APPENDIX

A–1 Common logarithms. In writing

$$10^3 = 1000$$
$$10^2 = 100$$
$$10^1 = 10$$
$$10^0 = 1$$
$$10^{-1} = 0.1$$
$$10^{-2} = 0.01$$
$$10^{-3} = 0.001$$

and considering this list as extending upward and downward indefinitely, we have a method for representing certain numbers as powers of ten. Although these special numbers are the only ones which can be written as 10 with an integral exponent, all positive numbers can be approximately represented as 10 with some exponent. This exponent we define as the *common logarithm** of the number or the *logarithm* of the number to the base ten.

Written in the form of an identity, this definition states $10^{\log x} \equiv x$, where log x is the abbreviation for the logarithm of x to the base 10. Thus log 1000 = 3, log 10 = 1, or log 0.001 = −3. More generally, by our definition, we would have $10^{\log (xy)} = xy$, or $10^{\log (x/y)} = x/y$.

As was stated, not only do the powers of ten listed above have logarithms, but all positive numbers do. The values of the logarithms of numbers every hundredth of a unit between 1 and 10 have been approximated to four decimal places in Table II. For example, to find log 7.63, we look down the first column N of the table for 7.6, and then move to the right of 7.6 to the number which appears in the column headed by 3. Finding .8825, we have log 7.63 = .8825, which means, of course, $10^{0.8825} = 7.63$ (approximately).

Actually, Table II, by the use of interpolation, gives the logarithm of a number with four significant digits. If N lies between x and

---

* There are other systems of logarithms, such as the natural logarithm system, with the irrational number $e = 2.718 \cdots$, for the base. In this discussion we are interested only in the system of common logarithms. Nor shall we define the logarithm of a negative number, although such exists in dealing with complex numbers.

$x + .01$, then $N = x + .01r$, with r between 0 and 1, so that

$$\log N = \log x + r[\log (x + .01) - \log x].*$$

EXAMPLE 1.   Find log 3.476.

Solution.   Since $3.47 < 3.476 < 3.48$, we have

$$\log 3.476 = \log 3.47 + .6(\log 3.48 - \log 3.47)$$
$$= .5403 + .6(.5416 - .5403)$$
$$= .5403 + .0008$$
$$= .5411.$$

This number can have only four significant figures, since the logarithms in the table are only four-figure approximations.

If the logarithm of a number is given to four decimal places, it is also possible to find the number using Table II.   If log N appears in the middle of the table, the process used to find N is reversed.   If log N lies between log x and log $(x + .01)$, then $N = x + .01r$ with

$$r = \frac{\log N - \log (x + .01)}{\log x - \log (x + .01)},$$

rounded to the nearest tenth.   (Why?)

EXAMPLE 2.   Find N if log $N = .7281$.

Solution.   Looking in the middle of the table, we find $.7275 < .7281 < .7284$, where

$$\log 5.35 = .7284,$$

$$\log 5.34 = .7275.$$

Therefore, we have

$$r = \frac{.7281 - .7275}{.7284 - .7275} = .7 \text{ (rounded off)},$$

and $N = 5.347$.

---

* This interpolation is called *linear interpolation*, or *interpolation by proportion*, since it assumes that the logarithm function is a straight line between x and $x + .01$.

Operations with logarithms, as well as the method for finding the logarithms of numbers larger than 10 or less than one which do not appear in Table II, depend on certain laws. We have, for any positive numbers x and y,

$$\log (xy) = \log x + \log y. \qquad \text{(A--1)}$$

Since, by definition,

$$x = 10^{\log x}, \qquad y = 10^{\log y},$$

we would have

$$xy = 10^{\log x + \log y}$$

by multiplying. But, by the definition of a logarithm, this statement is equivalent to

$$\log (xy) = \log x + \log y.$$

The second law under the same conditions is

$$\log (x/y) = \log x - \log y. \qquad \text{(A--2)}$$

This follows from an argument similar to that used for (A--1) except that division, rather than multiplication, is used. The third law states that for any positive numbers x and y, and any real p, $\log (x^p) = p \log x$. Again,

$$x = 10^{\log x}.$$

By raising each member of this equation to the pth power, we would have

$$x^p = 10^{p \log x},$$

but by the definition of a logarithm, this is equivalent to

$$\log (x^p) = p \log x. \qquad \text{(A--3)}$$

In general, the logarithm of N has two parts: a whole number, called the *characteristic*, and a positive decimal (a number n such that $0 \leq n < 1$), called the *mantissa*. If the decimal point in any number is just to the right of the first nonzero digit, the logarithm of that number has 0 for its characteristic. All the numbers between 1 and 10 found in Table II are of this type. Such a number is said to have its decimal point in *standard position*.

If any number is multiplied by 10, the decimal point is moved one place to the right, or if divided by 10, one place to the left. But each time a number is multiplied by 10, since

$$\log 10N = \log N + \log 10$$
$$= \log N + 1,$$

the logarithm of the number is increased by one. Likewise, if a number is divided by 10, its logarithm is decreased by one, for

$$\log \frac{N}{10} = \log N - \log 10$$
$$= \log N - 1.$$

Thus the general rule for obtaining the characteristic can be stated: The characteristic of the logarithm of a number is equal to the number of places the decimal point has been moved from standard position. The *characteristic* is positive if the point has been moved to the right, negative if to the left. The mantissa, that part of the logarithm which appears in the table, is not affected by the position of the decimal point in the number, but depends only on its succession of digits. Thus, using the result of Example 2, $\log 347.6 = 2.5411$, since its characteristic is 2, while $\log .003476 = -3 + .5411$. The characteristic -3 is usually written $7 - 10$ (it is common practice for computational purposes to write any negative characteristic as a positive integer minus a multiple of 10), so that $-3 + .5411 = 7.5411 - 10$.

EXAMPLE 3.   Use logarithms to compute $\dfrac{1280 \cdot 0.849}{62.8}$.

Solution.   By letting $N = \dfrac{1280 \cdot 0.849}{62.8}$, we have, using (A–1) and (A–2), $\log N = \log 1280 + \log 0.849 - \log 62.8$.   The work should then be clearly arranged as follows:

$$
\begin{aligned}
\log 1280 &= 3.1072 \\
(+) \log 0.849 &= \underline{9.9289 - 10} \\
\log \text{numerator} &= 13.0361 - 10 \\
(-) \log 62.8 &= \underline{1.7980} \\
\log N &= 11.2381 - 10 \\
N &= 17.3.
\end{aligned}
$$

N is given with three significant figures, since the original numbers were of this type.

EXAMPLE 4. Compute by using logarithms: $\sqrt{0.01278}/(0.4825)^3$.

Solution. We know $\log N = \frac{1}{2} \log 0.01278 - 3 \log 0.4825$. Again arranging our work:

$$\log 0.4825 = 9.6834 - 10$$
$$3 \log 0.4825 = 29.0502 - 30$$
$$= 9.0502 - 10$$

$$\log 0.01278 = 18.1065 - 20$$
$$\tfrac{1}{2} \log 0.01278 = 9.0532 - 10$$
$$(-)\, 3 \log 0.4825 = 9.0502 - 10$$
$$\log N = 0.0030$$
$$N = 1.007.$$

PROBLEMS

Using logarithms, compute the value of the following to the correct number of significant figures.

1. $(357)(87.2)$

2. $(47.2)(0.897)$

3. $\dfrac{(32.7)}{(0.892)^{1/2}}$

4. $\dfrac{(245)(8.62)}{(7.84)^2}$

5. $(32.79)(497.2)(9.738)$

6. $\sqrt{756.9}\,(4.796)$

7. $\dfrac{\sqrt{(738.2)}(38.74)}{(0.9576)^2(8743)}$

8. $\left[\dfrac{\sqrt{8453}\,(.002477)}{347.9}\right]^{1/2}$

A–2 Use of the trigonometric tables. There are two tables following this appendix which are used in connection with the circular functions. Table I lists the values of the sine, cosine, tangent, and cotangent, approximated to four decimal places, of angles at 10′ intervals in the first quadrant. From the values of the functions for these angles, given in both degree and radian measure, it is possible to find the functions of angles of any size. Table III gives the logarithms of these same values, and is constructed similarly.

Since the circular function of any angle is the same as the cofunction of the complementary angle, Table I is efficiently constructed so that angles from 0° to 45° are at the left, while angles from 45° to 90° are at the right. Moreover, the circular functions listed at the top go with the angles at the left, while those at the bottom go with the angles at the right.

For example, opposite 24°10′ and in the column under sine, we find .4094, which is sin 24°10′. The value for sin 68°20′ is .9293, which we find in the column above sine, since 68°20′ is given at the right.

As in Table II for logarithms, Table I may be interpolated to find the circular functions of other angles. If x and $x + 10'$ are consecutive angles in the table, and r is an integer between 0 and 10, we may approximate sin $(x + r')$ by interpolating by proportion:

$$\sin (x + r') = x + \frac{r}{10}[\sin (x + 10') - \sin x].$$

The other functions are found by similar formulas.

EXAMPLE 1. Find sin 24°16′.

Solution. Since the angle 24°16′ lies between 24°10′ and 24°20′,

$$\sin 24°16' = \sin 24°10' + \tfrac{6}{10}[\sin 24°20' - \sin 24°10']$$
$$= .4094 + \tfrac{6}{10}(.4120 - .4094)$$
$$= .4094 + .0016$$
$$= .4110.$$

EXAMPLE 2. Find cos 57°42′.

Solution. With 57°42′ between 57°40′ and 57°50′, we have

$$\cos 57°42' = \cos 57°40' + \tfrac{2}{10}[\cos 57°50' - \cos 57°40']$$
$$= .5348 + \tfrac{2}{10}(.5324 - .5348)$$
$$= .5348 - .0005$$
$$= .5343.$$

Table I may also be used to find the angle between 0° and 90° if the value of a circular function is given. For example, if tan θ = .9435, by looking in the tangent column we find the entry .9435 opposite 43°20′, and thus $\theta = 43°20'$.

The table may also be interpolated to find an angle, approximated to the nearest minute, when the value of a function of this angle lies between two entries in the table. If sin θ is given, we find two consecutive entries in the sine column between which the given value lies. Thus, letting $\theta = x + r'$, where r is some integer between

0 and 10, and x and $x + 10'$ are the consecutive entries in the table, we find r by using the approximation

$$\frac{r}{10} = \frac{\sin{(x + r')} - \sin{x}}{\sin{(x + 10')} - \sin{x}}.$$

Again, other functions follow the same pattern.

EXAMPLE 3. Find the angle θ between $0°$ and $90°$ if $\sin \theta = .6231$.

Solution. We locate .6231 in the sine column between $\sin 38°30' = .6225$ and $\sin 38°40' = .6248$. Thus

$$\frac{r}{10} = \frac{.6231 - .6225}{.6248 - .6225},$$

or

$$r = 10 \left(\frac{.0006}{.0023}\right)$$
$$= 3,$$

so that $\theta = 38°33'$, approximated to the nearest minute.

EXAMPLE 4. Find the angle θ, if $\cos \theta = .5741$.

Solution. We find $\cos 54°50' = .5760$, and $\cos 55° = .5736$. Therefore

$$\frac{r}{10} = \frac{.5741 - .5760}{.5736 - .5760},$$

so that

$$r = 10 \left(\frac{.0019}{.0024}\right)$$
$$= 8,$$

and our result is $\theta = 54°58'$.

Table III is used in the same way as Table I, and formulas need not be repeated.

PROBLEMS

1. Find the value of each of the following by using Table I:

(a) sin 14°20'   (b) tan 52°40'
(c) cos 28°50'   (d) sin 63°30'
(e) tan 21°10'   (f) cos 72°20'
(g) sin 115°30'   (h) cos 161°10'

2. Find the approximate value of each of the following by using Table I and interpolation:

(a) sin 72°43'   (b) cos 28°46'
(c) tan 51°29'   (d) cos 63°23'
(e) tan 39°18'   (f) sin 128°36'
(g) cos 153°17'   (h) sin 8°9'

3. Find the angle θ between 0° and 90° using Table I if:

(a) $\sin \theta = .4253$ (b) $\tan \theta = 1.1237$
(c) $\cos \theta = .8857$ (d) $\sin \theta = .8450$
(e) $\tan \theta = .2156$ (f) $\cos \theta = .2447$
(g) $\sin \theta = .3475$ (h) $\cos \theta = .7844$

4. Find the approximate value of θ to the nearest minute, by using Table I and interpolation, if:

(a) $\tan \theta = .8172$ (b) $\sin \theta = .5331$
(c) $\cos \theta = .2717$ (d) $\cos \theta = .9392$
(e) $\sin \theta = .7531$ (f) $\tan \theta = .8083$
(g) $\cos \theta = .5386$ (h) $\sin \theta = .9648$

5. Find the value of each of the following by using Table III, and interpolation if necessary, for the following:

(a) log sin 13°20'   (b) log cos 45°30'
(c) log sin 67°32'   (d) log cos 38°21'
(e) log tan 72°47'   (f) log sin 115°18'
(g) log cos 68°56'   (h) log sin 51°49'

6. Find the value of θ to the nearest minute by using Table III, and interpolation if necessary, for the following:

(a) $\log \sin \theta = 9.2870 - 10$ (b) $\log \cos \theta = 9.8365 - 10$
(c) $\log \tan \theta = 9.7353 - 10$ (d) $\log \cos \theta = 9.7316 - 10$
(e) $\log \sin \theta = 9.2278 - 10$ (f) $\log \tan \theta = .4937$
(g) $\log \cos \theta = 9.9797 - 10$ (h) $\log \sin \theta = 9.8761 - 10$

ANSWERS TO ODD-NUMBERED PROBLEMS

CHAPTER 1

ARTICLE 1–2

1. $-6.5, -5, -1, 0, 0.333, 1/3, \sqrt{4}, 2.3, 2^3$

5. $(0), (-1), (1), \left(\dfrac{\sqrt{2} + \sqrt{3}}{2}\right), \left(\dfrac{x_1 + x_2}{2}\right)$

7. (a) ± 2 (b) $\pm\sqrt{5}$ (c) ± 3 (d) $\pm 1/4$

    (e) $7, -3$ (f) 4 (g) $9, -3$ (h) $6, -4$

    (i) $6, -2$ (j) none   (k) none   (l) $8, 2$

11. $|x - a| = r$, or $\sqrt{(x - a)^2} = r$

ARTICLE 1–3

3. (a) $(3,2)$ (b) $(-4,6)$ (c) $(5,0)$

5. II, IV, III, I, II, IV

7. (a) $(8,4), (4,-4), (-4,4)$ (b) $(-1,6), (3,-2), (-3,-4)$

ARTICLE 1–4

1. (a) $\sqrt{34}$ (b) 106 (c) $3\sqrt{2}/4$

    (d) 13 (e) 8 (f) $\sqrt{(x + 1)^2 + (y - 3)^2}$

7. Yes; No

9. $(2\sqrt{3}, -1 - 4\sqrt{3})$ or $(-2\sqrt{3}, -1 + 4\sqrt{3})$

11. $(\pm a\sqrt{2}/2, 0)$ and $(0, \pm a\sqrt{2}/2)$

13. $(1,0), (0,-1), (1/\sqrt{2}, 1/\sqrt{2}), (-1/2, \sqrt{3}/2)$

ARTICLE 1–5

1. (a) $(x - 3)^2 + (y - 1)^2 = 25$ (b) $(x - 4)^2 + (y + 2)^2 = 9$

    (c) $(x + 1)^2 + (y - 3)^2 = 9$ (d) $(x - 2)^2 + (y + 4)^2 = 25$

3. (a) All points inside or on the circle

    (b) All points outside or on the circle

    (c) The point $(3,-1)$

5. $4\sqrt{3}r$

CHAPTER 2

ARTICLE 2–2

5. Problem 2: (a) $\frac{1}{8}$ (c) $-\frac{5}{8}$ (e) $\frac{2}{3}$ (g) 2

             (b) $\frac{3}{8}$ (d) $-\frac{5}{6}$ (f) $\frac{5}{4}$ (h) $-\frac{1}{3}$

   Problem 3: (a) $\frac{1}{12}$ (c) $\frac{1}{8}$ (e) $-\frac{3}{4}$ (g) $\frac{5}{24}$

             (b) $\frac{1}{3}$ (d) $\frac{2}{9}$ (f) $-\frac{5}{12}$ (h) $-\frac{5}{2}$

7. (a) .4712   (c) .8203   (e) -4.4186
    (b) 2.7285   (d) 3.3080   (f) -6.6116

9. (a) $47°41'$ (b) $33°53'$ (c) $51°$ (d) $151°$
    (e) $81°21'$ (f) $85°17'$ (g) $164°47'$ (h) $42°22'$
    (i) $212°37'$ (j) $206°12'$ (k) $37°38'$ (l) $4°26'$

11. 3/2 radians, $85°57'$ 13. $120°, 30°, 187°30', 108°30'$

15. 60 radians   17. $5, 1, \theta$

ARTICLE 2–3

1. $+$ 3. $+$ 5. $+$ 7. $-$

9. $-$ 11. $+$ 13. $+$ 15. $-$

17. I or IV   19. III or IV   21. I or IV   23. IV

25. II

27. $\sin \theta = 4/5$ 29. $\sin \theta = 3/5$
    $\cos \theta = 3/5$ $\cos \theta = -4/5$

31. $\sin \theta = -15/17$ 33. $\sin \theta = -1$
    $\cos \theta = -8/17$ $\cos \theta = 0$

35. $\sin \theta = 0$ 37. $\sin \theta = -3/5$
    $\cos \theta = 1$ $\tan \theta = 3/4$

39. $\cos \theta = -\sqrt{5}/3$ 41. $\sin \theta = -\sqrt{11}/6$
    $\tan \theta = -2/\sqrt{5}$ $\tan \theta = -\sqrt{11}/5$

43. $\cos \theta = -4/5$ 45. $\sin \theta = \pm 2/\sqrt{13}$
    $\tan \theta = 3/4$ $\cos \theta = \pm 3/\sqrt{13}$

47. $\cos \theta = \pm\sqrt{95}/12$ 49. $\sin \theta = -15/17$
    $\tan \theta = \pm 7/\sqrt{95}$ $\cos \theta = -8/17$

51. $\sin \theta = -15/17$
    $\cos \theta = -8/17$

ARTICLE 2–4

1. $\sin \theta = 0$ 3. $\sin \theta = 0$
    $\cos \theta = -1$ $\cos \theta = 1$

5. (a) $\sin \theta = 0$ (b) $\sin \theta = -1$ (c) $\sin \theta = 1$
       $\cos \theta = -1$ $\cos \theta = 0$ $\cos \theta = 0$

    (d) $\sin \theta = 0$ (e) $\sin \theta = 0$ (f) $\sin \theta = 0$
       $\cos \theta = 1$ $\cos \theta = -1$ $\cos \theta = 1$

    (g) $\sin \theta = 1$ (h) $\sin \theta = 0$ (i) $\sin \theta = 0$
       $\cos \theta = 0$ $\cos \theta = 1$ $\cos \theta = -1$

25. (a) $\sqrt{2}$ (b) 2

ARTICLE 2–5

11. (a) 1   (b) 1   13. $-\sqrt{3}$ 15. $\frac{5}{2} - \sqrt{3}$ 17. -1

19. 2   21. $30° = \pi/6$ 23. $30° = \pi/6$
                        $150° = 5\pi/6$ $210° = 7\pi/6$

25. $135° = 3\pi/4$
$315° = 7\pi/4$

27. $45° = \pi/4$
$135° = 3\pi/4$

29. $150° = 5\pi/6$
$330° = 11\pi/6$

CHAPTER 3

ARTICLE 3–3

1. $\sin 75° = \dfrac{\sqrt{6} + \sqrt{2}}{4}$, $\cos 75° = \dfrac{\sqrt{6} - \sqrt{2}}{4}$, $\tan 75° = 2 + \sqrt{3}$

3. $\cos \dfrac{7\pi}{12} = \dfrac{\sqrt{2} - \sqrt{6}}{4}$, $\tan \dfrac{7\pi}{12} = -(2 + \sqrt{3})$

5. (a) $56/65$ (b) $-33/65$ (c) $-56/33$
   (d) $-16/65$ (e) $63/65$ (f) $-16/63$

7. (a) II   (b) IV

9. $\sin (\alpha + \beta) = -304/425$, $\cos (\alpha + \beta) = 297/425$

11. $\dfrac{\sqrt{3} \tan \theta + 1}{\sqrt{3} - \tan \theta}$ 13. $\dfrac{1 - \tan \theta}{1 + \tan \theta}$

15. $\dfrac{2}{\sqrt{3} \sin \theta - \cos \theta}$ 17. $\dfrac{\sin \theta - \cos \theta}{\sqrt{2}}$

33. $13 \sin (\theta + \theta_1)$, where $\sin \theta_1 = 12/13$ and $\cos \theta_1 = 5/13$

35. $5 \sin (\theta + \theta_1)$, where $\sin \theta_1 = -3/5$ and $\cos \theta_1 = 4/5$

37. $2 \sin \left(\theta + \dfrac{\pi}{4}\right)$

ARTICLE 3–4

1. $-\sin 16°$ 3. $-\sin 41°$ 5. $-\cot 24°$
7. $\cos 5°$ 9. $-\cot 14°$ 11. $-\sin 16°18'$
13. $-\cos 24°46'$ 15. $\sin 23°21'$ 27. π

CHAPTER 4

ARTICLE 4–1

3. $33° = 15° + 18°$, $39° = 75° - 36°$, $42° = 60° - 18°$

5. $.10414 < \sin \pi/30 < .10472$, $1 > \cos \pi/30 > .99452$,
$.10472 < \tan \pi/30 < .10530$

ARTICLE 4–4

1. (a) $\beta = 52°40'$, $b = 319$, $c = 401$
   (b) $\beta = 27°20'$, $a = 1540$, $c = 1730$
   (c) $\alpha = 29°40'$, $\beta = 60°20'$, $c = 6.63$
   (d) $\alpha = 44°40'$, $\beta = 45°20'$, $a = 67.6$
   (e) $\alpha = 38°50'$, $a = .522$, $b = .648$

  (f) $\beta = 52°20'$, $b = 71.0$, $c = 89.7$
  (g) $\alpha = 33°30'$, $\beta = 56°30'$, $c = 68.7$
  (h) $\alpha = 48°35'$, $a = 2448$, $b = 2160$
  (i) $\alpha = 59°36'$, $\beta = 30°24'$, $b = 3185$
  (j) $\alpha = 23°10'$, $\beta = 66°50'$, $c = 8.320$
  (k) $\alpha = 27°3'$, $b = 1.619$, $c = 1.818$
  (l) $\alpha = 42°37'$, $a = 66.74$, $c = 98.58$
  (m) $\alpha = 42°30'$, $\beta = 47°30'$, $a = 3274$
  (n) $\beta = 65°13'$, $a = 147.0$, $c = 350.8$

3. 313 ft, $19°0'$ 5. 474 sq in   7. 55°
9. 7.075 in, 7.075 in, 10.62 in
11. 172 ft   13. 78.8 ft   15. 2770 ft
17. 6.30 mi from A, 9.09 mi from B
19. 3195 ft south, 3485 ft west.
21. (a) $v = 5$, $\theta = 53°$ (b) $v = 50$, $\theta = 63°$
  (c) $v = 32.9$, $\theta = 119°30'$ (d) $v = 858.2$, $\theta = 296°27'$
23. 56°, 22 ft/sec   25. N 47°0' W
27. (a) $f = 43$, $\theta = 122°$ (b) $f = 8250$, $\theta = 21°10'$ (c) $f = 3000$, $\theta = 255°$

ARTICLE 4–6

1. (a) $\gamma = 38°$, $b = 163$, $c = 102$
  (b) $\alpha = 40°26'$, $a = 36.27$, $b = 55.35$
  (c) $\beta = 13°52'$, $a = 270400$, $c = 321000$
  (d) $\alpha = 112°16'$, $a = 30.72$, $c = 26.56$
3. No.
5. (a) $\alpha_1 = 91°50'$, $\gamma_1 = 49°30'$, $a_1 = 95.0$
   $\alpha_2 = 10°50'$, $\gamma_2 = 130°30'$, $a_2 = 17.9$
  (b) $\beta = 127°40'$, $\gamma = 7°10'$, $b = 55.0$
  (c) $\alpha = 17°49'$, $\gamma = 14°24'$, $c = 11.96$
  (d) $\alpha = 76°42'$, $\beta = 46°0'$, $a = 6.667$
7. (a) $\beta = 31°19'$, $\gamma = 96°23'$, $a = 28.35$
  (b) $\alpha = 45°50'$, $\beta = 76°30'$, $c = 545$
9. (a) $\alpha = 41°$, $\beta = 56°$, $\gamma = 83°$
  (b) $\alpha = 30°$, $\beta = 63°$, $\gamma = 87°$
15. 29.80 in, 48.52 in 17. 100 mi, 60 mi   19. 25.5 ft
21. N 79°20' W   23. 148 mi/hr, S 63° E

CHAPTER 5

ARTICLE 5–2

3. $2\pi/3 \pm 2n\pi$ 5. $n\pi$ 7. $\pi/4 \pm 2n\pi$
9. $\pi/2$ 11. $-\pi/2$ 13. $(-1)^n 24° + n180°$

15. $51° \pm n360°$ 17. $84°20'$ 21. $\frac{1}{2}$ arc tan $y/3$
23. $\frac{1}{2}$ arc sec $y/2$ 27. $\frac{1}{4}(4 + \cos 3y)$ 29. $\tan (y + 2)$

31. $\dfrac{\cos \left(2y - \dfrac{\pi}{12} \right) - 1}{2}$

ARTICLE 5–3

1. $\pm 3/5$ 3. $\pm 12/5$ 5. $\sqrt{11}/6$
7. u 9. $\pm \sqrt{1 - u^2}/u$ 11. $\pi/7$
13. $\pi/18$ 15. $2\pi/5$ 17. 0
19. $uv \pm \sqrt{(1 - u^2)(1 - v^2)}$ 21. $\pm 3/5$
23. 1 or $-7/8$ 25. $-16/63$
27. $(24\sqrt{5} - 14)/75$ 37. $2n\pi \pm (\pi/2 - \theta)$
39. $n\pi + \theta$

ARTICLE 5–4

1. amp. 5, period 1   3. amp. 3, period 6
5. amp. 1.5, period $4\pi/3$ 7. amp. 2, period 8π
9. amp. .5, period $2\pi/3$ 11. amp. 100, period 200 (approx.)

ARTICLE 5–6

1. amp. 2, period 2π, phase displacement $\pi/6$
3. amp. 5, period π, phase displacement $\pi/16$
5. amp. 1, period 2π, phase displacement .25
7. amp. 1, period 2π, phase displacement 1.176
9. amp. 17, period 2π, phase displacement, .4900
11. amp. $\sqrt{29}$, period 2π, phase displacement, 1.1903
13. period 2π 15. period 4π 17. period 2π

CHAPTER 6

ARTICLE 6–1

1. $1/\sin \theta$ 3. $\pm \sqrt{1 - \sin^2 \theta}$
5. $\pm \sin \theta/\sqrt{1 - \sin^2 \theta}$ 7. $1/\cos \theta$
9. $\pm \sqrt{1 - \cos^2 \theta}$ 11. $\pm \sqrt{1 - \cos^2 \theta}/\cos \theta$
13. $\sin \theta = \pm \tan \theta/\sqrt{1 + \tan^2 \theta}$, $\cos \theta = \pm 1/\sqrt{1 + \tan^2 \theta}$
    $\cot \theta = 1/\tan \theta$, $\sec \theta = \pm \sqrt{1 + \tan^2 \theta}$, $\csc \theta = \pm \sqrt{1 + \tan^2 \theta}/\tan \theta$
15. $1/(1 - \cos^2 \theta)$

ARTICLE 6–2

3. $\sin 7\pi/12 = \sqrt{2 + \sqrt{3}}/2$, $\cos 7\pi/12 = -\sqrt{2 - \sqrt{3}}/2$, $\tan 7\pi 12 = -(2 + \sqrt{3})$

5. (a) $-120/169$ (b) $-119/169$ (c) $120/119$
    (d) $3/\sqrt{13}$ (e) $2/\sqrt{13}$ (f) $3/2$

7. $\dfrac{3 + 4\cos 2\theta + \cos 4\theta}{8}$

ARTICLE 6–3

1. $(\sin 8\theta - \sin 2\theta)/2$ 3. $(\sin 12\theta - \sin 2\theta)/2$
5. $(\sin 7\theta + \sin 3\theta)/2$ 7. $[\sin(3\theta/2) - \sin(\theta 2)]/2$
9. $2\sin(\pi/6)\cos(\pi/18)$ 11. $2\cos(\pi/2)\cos(5\pi/18)$
13. $2\sin 6\theta \cos 2\theta$ 15. $2\cos(5\theta/4)\sin(5\theta/12)$

ARTICLE 6–4

1. $\left(\dfrac{(-1)^n}{6} + n\right)\pi$, $\left(\dfrac{(-1)^{n+1}}{6} + n\right)\pi$

3. $(\pm\frac{1}{4} + 2n)\pi$, $(\pm\frac{3}{4} + 2n)\pi$ 5. $(\pm\frac{1}{6} + n)\pi$

7. $(\frac{1}{2} + n)\pi$, $(\pm\frac{1}{3} + 2n)\pi$ 9. $n180°$, $-26°34' + n180°$

11. $\left(\dfrac{(-1)^n}{2} + n\right)\pi$, $\left(\dfrac{(-1)^{n+1}}{6} + n\right)\pi$

13. None   15. $\left(\dfrac{(-1)^{n+1}}{6} + n\right)\pi$

17. $33°41' + n180°$, $-45° + n180°$ 19. $\pm 18° + n180°$, $\pm 54° + n180°$

21. $\left(\dfrac{(-1)^{n+1}}{2} + n\right)\dfrac{\pi}{6}$ 23. $\left(\dfrac{(-1)^n}{6} + n\right)\pi$, $\left(\dfrac{(-1)^{n+1}}{2} + n\right)\pi$

25. $(\frac{1}{2} + n)\pi$ 27. $(\pm\frac{1}{6} + n)\pi$

29. $\left(\frac{1}{6} + \dfrac{(-1)^{n+1}}{2} + n\right)\pi$ 31. $\left(\dfrac{(-1)^n - 1}{4} + n\right)\pi$

33. 3   35. none

CHAPTER 7

ARTICLE 7–2

7. $(6,8)$ 9. $(-1,1)$ 11. $(3,11)$
13. $(-\frac{1}{2},-\frac{1}{2})$ 15. $(1,0)$ 17. (a) $13 + 18i$, (b) $3 + 22i$
19. (a) $-i$ (b) 1 (c) i (d) $-i$

ARTICLE 7–3

1. (a) $2(\cos 0° + i \sin 0°)$
   (b) $2(\cos 180° + i \sin 180°)$
   (c) $3(\cos 90° + i \sin 90°)$
   (d) $\cos 270° + i \sin 270°$
   (e) $2\sqrt{2}(\cos 315° + i \sin 315°)$
   (f) $2\sqrt{2}(\cos 135° + i \sin 135°)$
   (g) $\cos 120° + i \sin 120°$
   (h) $\cos 240° + i \sin 240°$

3. (a) $6i$ (b) $-4\sqrt{3} - 4i$ (c) $12i$
   (d) 8

5. (a) $\sqrt{3} + i$ (b) $-1 + \sqrt{3}i$

ARTICLE 7–4

1. $64i$

3. $-4\sqrt{2} - 4\sqrt{2}i$

5. $\dfrac{\sqrt{3}}{2} + \dfrac{i}{2}$

7. 1

9. $-2\sqrt{2} + 2\sqrt{2}i,\ 2\sqrt{2} - 2\sqrt{2}i$

11. $1 + \sqrt{3}i,\ -2,\ 1 - \sqrt{3}i$

13. $\sqrt{3} + i,\ -1 + \sqrt{3}i,\ -\sqrt{3} - i,\ 1 - \sqrt{3}i$

15. $(\cos 36° + i \sin 36°),\ (\cos 72° + i \sin 72°),\ \ldots$

17. $1,\ i,\ -1,\ -i$

19. $\dfrac{\sqrt{5} + 1}{2} + \sqrt{\dfrac{5 - \sqrt{5}}{2}}\, i,$

$\dfrac{1 - \sqrt{5}}{2} + \sqrt{\dfrac{5 + \sqrt{5}}{2}}\, i,$

$-2,$

$\dfrac{1 - \sqrt{5}}{2} - \sqrt{\dfrac{5 + \sqrt{5}}{2}}\, i,$

$\dfrac{\sqrt{5} + 1}{2} - \sqrt{\dfrac{5 - \sqrt{5}}{2}}\, i$

CHAPTER 8

ARTICLE 8–1

1. P_x has an x-coordinate, $x = a \cos \omega t$

3. Yes; period π.

5. $E = 8 \sin 120\pi t$

7. $y = .001 \sin 800\pi t$

ARTICLE 8–2

1. amp., a

3. $A_0 = 80,\ A_1 = 9.5,\ A_2 = 1.44,\ \alpha_1 = .53,\ \alpha_2 = 2.16$

ANSWERS TO THE APPENDIX

ARTICLE A–1

1. 31100   2. 42.3   3. 34.6   4. 34.4

5. 158800   6. 131.9   7. .1312   8. .02559

ARTICLE A–2

1. (a) .2476   (b) 1.3111
   (c) .8760   (d) .8949
   (e) .3872   (f) .3035
   (g) .9026   (h) −.9465

2. (a) .9549   (b) .8766
   (c) 1.2565   (d) .4480
   (e) .8185   (f) .7815
   (g) −.8932   (h) .1418

3. (a) 25°10′   (b) 48°20′
   (c) 27°40′   (d) 57°40′
   (e) 12°10′   (f) 75°50′
   (g) 20°20′   (h) 38°20′

4. (a) 39°15′   (b) 32°13′
   (c) 74°14′   (d) 20°5′
   (e) 48°51′   (f) 38°57′
   (g) 57°25′   (h) 74°45′

5. (a) 9.3629 − 10   (b) 9.8457 − 10
   (c) 9.9657 − 10   (d) 9.8944 − 10
   (e) .5089   (f) 9.9562 − 10
   (g) 9.5556 − 10   (h) 9.8954 − 10

6. (a) 11°10′   (b) 46°40′
   (c) 28°32′   (d) 57°23′
   (e) 9°44′   (f) 72°13′
   (g) 17°22′   (h) 48°45′

TABLE I
Values of Trigonometric Functions   141

Degrees	Radians	Sine	Tangent	Cotangent	Cosine		
0° 00′	.0000	.0000	.0000		1.0000	1.5708	90° 00′
10′	.0029	.0029	.0029	343.77	1.0000	1.5679	50′
20′	.0058	.0058	.0058	171.89	1.0000	1.5650	40′
30′	.0087	.0087	.0087	114.59	1.0000	1.5621	30′
40′	.0116	.0116	.0116	85.940	.9999	1.5592	20′
50′	.0145	.0145	.0145	68.750	.9999	1.5563	10′
1° 00′	.0175	.0175	.0175	57.290	.9998	1.5533	89° 00′
10′	.0204	.0204	.0204	49.104	.9998	1.5504	50′
20′	.0233	.0233	.0233	42.964	.9997	1.5475	40′
30′	.0262	.0262	.0262	38.188	.9997	1.5446	30′
40′	.0291	.0291	.0291	34.368	.9996	1.5417	20′
50′	.0320	.0320	.0320	31.242	.9995	1.5388	10′
2° 00′	.0349	.0349	.0349	28.636	.9994	1.5359	88° 00′
10′	.0378	.0378	.0378	26.432	.9993	1.5330	50′
20′	.0407	.0407	.0407	24.542	.9992	1.5301	40′
30′	.0436	.0436	.0437	22.904	.9990	1.5272	30′
40′	.0465	.0465	.0466	21.470	.9989	1.5243	20′
50′	.0495	.0494	.0495	20.206	.9988	1.5213	10′
3° 00′	.0524	.0523	.0524	19.081	.9986	1.5184	87° 00′
10′	.0553	.0552	.0553	18.075	.9985	1.5155	50′
20′	.0582	.0581	.0582	17.169	.9983	1.5126	40′
30′	.0611	.0610	.0612	16.350	.9981	1.5097	30′
40′	.0640	.0640	.0641	15.605	.9980	1.5068	20′
50′	.0669	.0669	.0670	14.924	.9978	1.5039	10′
4° 00′	.0698	.0698	.0699	14.301	.9976	1.5010	86° 00′
10′	.0727	.0727	.0729	13.727	.9974	1.4981	50′
20′	.0756	.0756	.0758	13.197	.9971	1.4952	40′
30′	.0785	.0785	.0787	12.706	.9969	1.4923	30′
40′	.0814	.0814	.0816	12.251	.9967	1.4893	20′
50′	.0844	.0843	.0846	11.826	.9964	1.4864	10′
5° 00′	.0873	.0872	.0875	11.430	.9962	1.4835	85° 00′
10′	.0902	.0901	.0904	11.059	.9959	1.4806	50′
20′	.0931	.0929	.0934	10.712	.9957	1.4777	40′
30′	.0960	.0958	.0963	10.385	.9954	1.4748	30′
40′	.0989	.0987	.0992	10.078	.9951	1.4719	20′
50′	.1018	.1016	.1022	9.7882	.9948	1.4690	10′
6° 00′	.1047	.1045	.1051	9.5144	.9945	1.4661	84° 00′
10′	.1076	.1074	.1080	9.2553	.9942	1.4632	50′
20′	.1105	.1103	.1110	9.0098	.9939	1.4603	40′
30′	.1134	.1132	.1139	8.7769	.9936	1.4573	30′
40′	.1164	.1161	.1169	8.5555	.9932	1.4544	20′
50′	.1193	.1190	.1198	8.3450	.9929	1.4515	10′
7° 00′	.1222	.1219	.1228	8.1443	.9925	1.4486	83° 00′
10′	.1251	.1248	.1257	7.9530	.9922	1.4457	50′
20′	.1280	.1276	.1287	7.7704	.9918	1.4428	40′
30′	.1309	.1305	.1317	7.5958	.9914	1.4399	30′
40′	.1338	.1334	.1346	7.4287	.9911	1.4370	20′
50′	.1367	.1363	.1376	7.2687	.9907	1.4341	10′
8° 00′	.1396	.1392	.1405	7.1154	.9903	1.4312	82° 00′
10′	.1425	.1421	.1435	6.9682	.9899	1.4283	50′
20′	.1454	.1449	.1465	6.8269	.9894	1.4254	40′
30′	.1484	.1478	.1495	6.6912	.9890	1.4224	30′
40′	.1513	.1507	.1524	6.5606	.9886	1.4195	20′
50′	.1542	.1536	.1554	6.4348	.9881	1.4166	10′
9° 00′	.1571	.1564	.1584	6.3138	.9877	1.4137	81° 00′
		Cosine	Cotangent	Tangent	Sine	Radians	Degrees

TABLE I (Continued)
Values of Trigonometric Functions

Degrees	Radians	Sine	Tangent	Cotangent	Cosine		
9° 00′	.1571	.1564	.1584	6.3138	.9877	1.4137	81° 00′
10′	.1600	.1593	.1614	6.1970	.9872	1.4108	50′
20′	.1629	.1622	.1644	6.0844	.9868	1.4079	40′
30′	.1658	.1650	.1673	5.9758	.9863	1.4050	30′
40′	.1687	.1679	.1703	5.8708	.9858	1.4021	20′
50′	.1716	.1708	.1733	5.7694	.9853	1.3992	10′
10° 00′	.1745	.1736	.1763	5.6713	.9848	1.3963	80° 00′
10′	.1774	.1765	.1793	5.5764	.9843	1.3934	50′
20′	.1804	.1794	.1823	5.4845	.9838	1.3904	40′
30′	.1833	.1822	.1853	5.3955	.9833	1.3875	30′
40′	.1862	.1851	.1883	5.3093	.9827	1.3846	20′
50′	.1891	.1880	.1914	5.2257	.9822	1.3817	10′
11° 00′	.1920	.1908	.1944	5.1446	.9816	1.3788	79° 00′
10′	.1949	.1937	.1974	5.0658	.9811	1.3759	50′
20′	.1978	.1965	.2004	4.9894	.9805	1.3730	40′
30′	.2007	.1994	.2035	4.9152	.9799	1.3701	30′
40′	.2036	.2022	.2065	4.8430	.9793	1.3672	20′
50′	.2065	.2051	.2095	4.7729	.9787	1.3643	10′
12° 00′	.2094	.2079	.2126	4.7046	.9781	1.3614	78° 00′
10′	.2123	.2108	.2156	4.6382	.9775	1.3584	50′
20′	.2153	.2136	.2186	4.5736	.9769	1.3555	40′
30′	.2182	.2164	.2217	4.5107	.9763	1.3526	30′
40′	.2211	.2193	.2247	4.4494	.9757	1.3497	20′
50′	.2240	.2221	.2278	4.3897	.9750	1.3468	10′
13° 00′	.2269	.2250	.2309	4.3315	.9744	1.3439	77° 00′
10′	.2298	.2278	.2339	4.2747	.9737	1.3410	50′
20′	.2327	.2306	.2370	4.2193	.9730	1.3381	40′
30′	.2356	.2334	.2401	4.1653	.9724	1.3352	30′
40′	.2385	.2363	.2432	4.1126	.9717	1.3323	20′
50′	.2414	.2391	.2462	4.0611	.9710	1.3294	10′
14° 00′	.2443	.2419	.2493	4.0108	.9703	1.3265	76° 00′
10′	.2473	.2447	.2524	3.9617	.9696	1.3235	50′
20′	.2502	.2476	.2555	3.9136	.9689	1.3206	40′
30′	.2531	.2504	.2586	3.8667	.9681	1.3177	30′
40′	.2560	.2532	.2617	3.8208	.9674	1.3148	20′
50′	.2589	.2560	.2648	3.7760	.9667	1.3119	10′
15° 00′	.2618	.2588	.2679	3.7321	.9659	1.3090	75° 00′
10′	.2647	.2616	.2711	3.6891	.9652	1.3061	50′
20′	.2676	.2644	.2742	3.6470	.9644	1.3032	40′
30′	.2705	.2672	.2773	3.6059	.9636	1.3003	30′
40′	.2734	.2700	.2805	3.5656	.9628	1.2974	20′
50′	.2763	.2728	.2836	3.5261	.9621	1.2945	10′
16° 00′	.2793	.2756	.2867	3.4874	.9613	1.2915	74° 00′
10′	.2822	.2784	.2899	3.4495	.9605	1.2886	50′
20′	.2851	.2812	.2931	3.4124	.9596	1.2857	40′
30′	.2880	.2840	.2962	3.3759	.9588	1.2828	30′
40′	.2909	.2868	.2994	3.3402	.9580	1.2799	20′
50′	.2938	.2896	.3026	3.3052	.9572	1.2770	10′
17° 00′	.2967	.2924	.3057	3.2709	.9563	1.2741	73° 00′
10′	.2996	.2952	.3089	3.2371	.9555	1.2712	50′
20′	.3025	.2979	.3121	3.2041	.9546	1.2683	40′
30′	.3054	.3007	.3153	3.1716	.9537	1.2654	30′
40′	.3083	.3035	.3185	3.1397	.9528	1.2625	20′
50′	.3113	.3062	.3217	3.1084	.9520	1.2595	10′
18° 00′	.3142	.3090	.3249	3.0777	.9511	1.2566	72° 00′
		Cosine	Cotangent	Tangent	Sine	Radians	Degrees

TABLE I (Continued)
Values of Trigonometric Functions

Degrees	Radians	Sine	Tangent	Cotangent	Cosine		
18° 00′	.3142	.3090	.3249	3.0777	.9511	1.2566	72° 00′
10′	.3171	.3118	.3281	3.0475	.9502	1.2537	50′
20′	.3200	.3145	.3314	3.0178	.9492	1.2508	40′
30′	.3229	.3173	.3346	2.9887	.9483	1.2479	30′
40′	.3258	.3201	.3378	2.9600	.9474	1.2450	20′
50′	.3287	.3228	.3411	2.9319	.9465	1.2421	10′
19° 00′	.3316	.3256	.3443	2.9042	.9455	1.2392	71° 00′
10′	.3345	.3283	.3476	2.8770	.9446	1.2363	50′
20′	.3374	.3311	.3508	2.8502	.9436	1.2334	40′
30′	.3403	.3338	.3541	2.8239	.9426	1.2305	30′
40′	.3432	.3365	.3574	2.7980	.9417	1.2275	20′
50′	.3462	.3393	.3607	2.7725	.9407	1.2246	10′
20° 00′	.3491	.3420	.3640	2.7475	.9397	1.2217	70° 00′
10′	.3520	.3448	.3673	2.7228	.9387	1.2188	50′
20′	.3549	.3475	.3706	2.6985	.9377	1.2159	40′
30′	.3578	.3502	.3739	2.6746	.9367	1.2130	30′
40′	.3607	.3529	.3772	2.6511	.9356	1.2101	20′
50′	.3636	.3557	.3805	2.6279	.9346	1.2072	10′
21° 00′	.3665	.3584	.3839	2.6051	.9336	1.2043	69° 00′
10′	.3694	.3611	.3872	2.5826	.9325	1.2014	50′
20′	.3723	.3638	.3906	2.5605	.9315	1.1985	40′
30′	.3752	.3665	.3939	2.5386	.9304	1.1956	30′
40′	.3782	.3692	.3973	2.5172	.9293	1.1926	20′
50′	.3811	.3719	.4006	2.4960	.9283	1.1897	10′
22° 00′	.3840	.3746	.4040	2.4751	.9272	1.1868	68° 00′
10′	.3869	.3773	.4074	2.4545	.9261	1.1839	50′
20′	.3898	.3800	.4108	2.4342	.9250	1.1810	40′
30′	.3927	.3827	.4142	2.4142	.9239	1.1781	30′
40′	.3956	.3854	.4176	2.3945	.9228	1.1752	20′
50′	.3985	.3881	.4210	2.3750	.9216	1.1723	10′
23° 00′	.4014	.3907	.4245	2.3559	.9205	1.1694	67° 00′
10′	.4043	.3934	.4279	2.3369	.9194	1.1665	50′
20′	.4072	.3961	.4314	2.3183	.9182	1.1636	40′
30′	.4102	.3987	.4348	2.2998	.9171	1.1606	30′
40′	.4131	.4014	.4383	2.2817	.9159	1.1577	20′
50′	.4160	.4041	.4417	2.2637	.9147	1.1548	10′
24° 00′	.4189	.4067	.4452	2.2460	.9135	1.1519	66° 00′
10′	.4218	.4094	.4487	2.2286	.9124	1.1490	50′
20′	.4247	.4120	.4522	2.2113	.9112	1.1461	40′
30′	.4276	.4147	.4557	2.1943	.9100	1.1432	30′
40′	.4305	.4173	.4592	2.1775	.9088	1.1403	20′
50′	.4334	.4200	.4628	2.1609	.9075	1.1374	10′
25° 00′	.4363	.4226	.4663	2.1445	.9063	1.1345	65° 00′
10′	.4392	.4253	.4699	2.1283	.9051	1.1316	50′
20′	.4422	.4279	.4734	2.1123	.9038	1.1286	40′
30′	.4451	.4305	.4770	2.0965	.9026	1.1257	30′
40′	.4480	.4331	.4806	2.0809	.9013	1.1228	20′
50′	.4509	.4358	.4841	2.0655	.9001	1.1199	10′
26° 00′	.4538	.4384	.4877	2.0503	.8988	1.1170	64° 00′
10′	.4567	.4410	.4913	2.0353	.8975	1.1141	50′
20′	.4596	.4436	.4950	2.0204	.8962	1.1112	40′
30′	.4625	.4462	.4986	2.0057	.8949	1.1083	30′
40′	.4654	.4488	.5022	1.9912	.8936	1.1054	20′
50′	.4683	.4514	.5059	1.9768	.8923	1.1025	10′
27° 00′	.4712	.4540	.5095	1.9626	.8910	1.0996	63° 00′
		Cosine	Cotangent	Tangent	Sine	Radians	Degrees

TABLE I (Continued)
144
Values of Trigonometric Functions

Degrees	Radians	Sine	Tangent	Cotangent	Cosine		
27° 00′	.4712	.4540	.5095	1.9626	.8910	1.0996	63° 00′
10′	.4741	.4566	.5132	1.9486	.8897	1.0966	50′
20′	.4771	.4592	.5169	1.9347	.8884	1.0937	40′
30′	.4800	.4617	.5206	1.9210	.8870	1.0908	30′
40′	.4829	.4643	.5243	1.9074	.8857	1.0879	20′
50′	.4858	.4669	.5280	1.8940	.8843	1.0850	10′
28° 00′	.4887	.4695	.5317	1.8807	.8829	1.0821	62° 00′
10′	.4916	.4720	.5354	1.8676	.8816	1.0792	50′
20′	.4945	.4746	.5392	1.8546	.8802	1.0763	40′
30′	.4974	.4772	.5430	1.8418	.8788	1.0734	30′
40′	.5003	.4797	.5467	1.8291	.8774	1.0705	20′
50′	.5032	.4823	.5505	1.8165	.8760	1.0676	10′
29° 00′	.5061	.4848	.5543	1.8040	.8746	1.0647	61° 00′
10′	.5091	.4874	.5581	1.7917	.8732	1.0617	50′
20′	.5120	.4899	.5619	1.7796	.8718	1.0588	40′
30′	.5149	.4924	.5658	1.7675	.8704	1.0559	30′
40′	.5178	.4950	.5696	1.7556	.8689	1.0530	20′
50′	.5207	.4975	.5735	1.7437	.8675	1.0501	10′
30° 00′	.5236	.5000	.5774	1.7321	.8660	1.0472	60° 00′
10′	.5265	.5025	.5812	1.7205	.8646	1.0443	50′
20′	.5294	.5050	.5851	1.7090	.8631	1.0414	40′
30′	.5323	.5075	.5890	1.6977	.8616	1.0385	30′
40′	.5352	.5100	.5930	1.6864	.8601	1.0356	20′
50′	.5381	.5125	.5969	1.6753	.8587	1.0327	10′
31° 00′	.5411	.5150	.6009	1.6643	.8572	1.0297	59° 00′
10′	.5440	.5175	.6048	1.6534	.8557	1.0268	50′
20′	.5469	.5200	.6088	1.6426	.8542	1.0239	40′
30′	.5498	.5225	.6128	1.6319	.8526	1.0210	30′
40′	.5527	.5250	.6168	1.6212	.8511	1.0181	20′
50′	.5556	.5275	.6208	1.6107	.8496	1.0152	10′
32° 00′	.5585	.5299	.6249	1.6003	.8480	1.0123	58° 00′
10′	.5614	.5324	.6289	1.5900	.8465	1.0094	50′
20′	.5643	.5348	.6330	1.5798	.8450	1.0065	40′
30′	.5672	.5373	.6371	1.5697	.8434	1.0036	30′
40′	.5701	.5398	.6412	1.5597	.8418	1.0007	20′
50′	.5730	.5422	.6453	1.5497	.8403	.9977	10′
33° 00′	.5760	.5446	.6494	1.5399	.8387	.9948	57° 00′
10′	.5789	.5471	.6536	1.5301	.8371	.9919	50′
20′	.5818	.5495	.6577	1.5204	.8355	.9890	40′
30′	.5847	.5519	.6619	1.5108	.8339	.9861	30′
40′	.5876	.5544	.6661	1.5013	.8323	.9832	20′
50′	.5905	.5568	.6703	1.4919	.8307	.9803	10′
34° 00′	.5934	.5592	.6745	1.4826	.8290	.9774	56° 00′
10′	.5963	.5616	.6787	1.4733	.8274	.9745	50′
20′	.5992	.5640	.6830	1.4641	.8258	.9716	40′
30′	.6021	.5664	.6873	1.4550	.8241	.9687	30′
40′	.6050	.5688	.6916	1.4460	.8225	.9657	20′
50′	.6080	.5712	.6959	1.4370	.8208	.9628	10′
35° 00′	.6109	.5736	.7002	1.4281	.8192	.9599	55° 00′
10′	.6138	.5760	.7046	1.4193	.8175	.9570	50′
20′	.6167	.5783	.7089	1.4106	.8158	.9541	40′
30′	.6196	.5807	.7133	1.4019	.8141	.9512	30′
40′	.6225	.5831	.7177	1.3934	.8124	.9483	20′
50′	.6254	.5854	.7221	1.3848	.8107	.9454	10′
36° 00′	.6283	.5878	.7265	1.3764	.8090	.9425	54° 00′
		Cosine	Cotangent	Tangent	Sine	Radians	Degrees

TABLE I (Continued)
Values of Trigonometric Functions

Degrees	Radians	Sine	Tangent	Cotangent	Cosine		
36° 00′	.6283	.5878	.7265	1.3764	.8090	.9425	54° 00′
10′	.6312	.5901	.7310	1.3680	.8073	.9396	50′
20′	.6341	.5925	.7355	1.3597	.8056	.9367	40′
30′	.6370	.5948	.7400	1.3514	.8039	.9338	30′
40′	.6400	.5972	.7445	1.3432	.8021	.9308	20′
50′	.6429	.5995	.7490	1.3351	.8004	.9279	10′
37° 00′	.6458	.6018	.7536	1.3270	.7986	.9250	53° 00′
10′	.6487	.6041	.7581	1.3190	.7969	.9221	50′
20′	.6516	.6065	.7627	1.3111	.7951	.9192	40′
30′	.6545	.6088	.7673	1.3032	.7934	.9163	30′
40′	.6574	.6111	.7720	1.2954	.7916	.9134	20′
50′	.6603	.6134	.7766	1.2876	.7898	.9105	10′
38° 00′	.6632	.6157	.7813	1.2799	.7880	.9076	52° 00′
10′	.6661	.6180	.7860	1.2723	.7862	.9047	50′
20′	.6690	.6202	.7907	1.2647	.7844	.9018	40′
30′	.6720	.6225	.7954	1.2572	.7826	.8988	30′
40′	.6749	.6248	.8002	1.2497	.7808	.8959	20′
50′	.6778	.6271	.8050	1.2423	.7790	.8930	10′
39° 00′	.6807	.6293	.8098	1.2349	.7771	.8901	51° 00′
10′	.6836	.6316	.8146	1.2276	.7753	.8872	50′
20′	.6865	.6338	.8195	1.2203	.7735	.8843	40′
30′	.6894	.6361	.8243	1.2131	.7716	.8814	30′
40′	.6923	.6383	.8292	1.2059	.7698	.8785	20′
50′	.6952	.6406	.8342	1.1988	.7679	.8756	10′
40° 00′	.6981	.6428	.8391	1.1918	.7660	.8727	50° 00′
10′	.7010	.6450	.8441	1.1847	.7642	.8698	50′
20′	.7039	.6472	.8491	1.1778	.7623	.8668	40′
30′	.7069	.6494	.8541	1.1708	.7604	.8639	30′
40′	.7098	.6517	.8591	1.1640	.7585	.8610	20′
50′	.7127	.6539	.8642	1.1571	.7566	.8581	10′
41° 00′	.7156	.6561	.8693	1.1504	.7547	.8552	49° 00′
10′	.7185	.6583	.8744	1.1436	.7528	.8523	50′
20′	.7214	.6604	.8796	1.1369	.7509	.8494	40′
30′	.7243	.6626	.8847	1.1303	.7490	.8465	30′
40′	.7272	.6648	.8899	1.1237	.7470	.8436	20′
50′	.7301	.6670	.8952	1.1171	.7451	.8407	10′
42° 00′	.7330	.6691	.9004	1.1106	.7431	.8378	48° 00′
10′	.7359	.6713	.9057	1.1041	.7412	.8348	50′
20′	.7389	.6734	.9110	1.0977	.7392	.8319	40′
30′	.7418	.6756	.9163	1.0913	.7373	.8290	30′
40′	.7447	.6777	.9217	1.0850	.7353	.8261	20′
50′	.7476	.6799	.9271	1.0786	.7333	.8232	10′
43° 00′	.7505	.6820	.9325	1.0724	.7314	.8203	47° 00′
10′	.7534	.6841	.9380	1.0661	.7294	.8174	50′
20′	.7563	.6862	.9435	1.0599	.7274	.8145	40′
30′	.7592	.6884	.9490	1.0538	.7254	.8116	30′
40′	.7621	.6905	.9545	1.0477	.7234	.8087	20′
50′	.7650	.6926	.9601	1.0416	.7214	.8058	10′
44° 00′	.7679	.6947	.9657	1.0355	.7193	.8029	46° 00′
10′	.7709	.6967	.9713	1.0295	.7173	.7999	50′
20′	.7738	.6988	.9770	1.0235	.7153	.7970	40′
30′	.7767	.7009	.9827	1.0176	.7133	.7941	30′
40′	.7796	.7030	.9884	1.0117	.7112	.7912	20′
50′	.7825	.7050	.9942	1.0058	.7092	.7883	10′
45° 00′	.7854	.7071	1.0000	1.0000	.7071	.7854	45° 00′
		Cosine	Cotangent	Tangent	Sine	Radians	Degrees

TABLE II
Logarithms of Numbers

N	0	1	2	3	4	5	6	7	8	9
1.0	.0000	.0043	.0086	.0128	.0170	.0212	.0253	.0294	.0334	.0374
1.1	.0414	.0453	.0492	.0531	.0569	.0607	.0645	.0682	.0719	.0755
1.2	.0792	.0828	.0864	.0899	.0934	.0969	.1004	.1038	.1072	.1106
1.3	.1139	.1173	.1206	.1239	.1271	.1303	.1335	.1367	.1399	.1430
1.4	.1461	.1492	.1523	.1553	.1584	.1614	.1644	.1673	.1703	.1732
1.5	.1761	.1790	.1818	.1847	.1875	.1903	.1931	.1959	.1987	.2014
1.6	.2041	.2068	.2095	.2122	.2148	.2175	.2201	.2227	.2253	.2279
1.7	.2304	.2330	.2355	.2380	.2405	.2430	.2455	.2480	.2504	.2529
1.8	.2553	.2577	.2601	.2625	.2648	.2672	.2695	.2718	.2742	.2765
1.9	.2788	.2810	.2833	.2856	.2878	.2900	.2923	.2945	.2967	.2989
2.0	.3010	.3032	.3054	.3075	.3096	.3118	.3139	.3160	.3181	.3201
2.1	.3222	.3243	.3263	.3284	.3304	.3324	.3345	.3365	.3385	.3404
2.2	.3424	.3444	.3464	.3483	.3502	.3522	.3541	.3560	.3579	.3598
2.3	.3617	.3636	.3655	.3674	.3692	.3711	.3729	.3747	.3766	.3784
2.4	.3802	.3820	.3838	.3856	.3874	.3892	.3909	.3927	.3945	.3962
2.5	.3979	.3997	.4014	.4031	.4048	.4065	.4082	.4099	.4116	.4133
2.6	.4150	.4166	.4183	.4200	.4216	.4232	.4249	.4265	.4281	.4298
2.7	.4314	.4330	.4346	.4362	.4378	.4393	.4409	.4425	.4440	.4456
2.8	.4472	.4487	.4502	.4518	.4533	.4548	.4564	.4579	.4594	.4609
2.9	.4624	.4639	.4654	.4669	.4683	.4698	.4713	.4728	.4742	.4757
3.0	.4771	.4786	.4800	.4814	.4829	.4843	.4857	.4871	.4886	.4900
3.1	.4914	.4928	.4942	.4955	.4969	.4983	.4997	.5011	.5024	.5038
3.2	.5051	.5065	.5079	.5092	.5105	.5119	.5132	.5145	.5159	.5172
3.3	.5185	.5198	.5211	.5224	.5237	.5250	.5263	.5276	.5289	.5302
3.4	.5315	.5328	.5340	.5353	.5366	.5378	.5391	.5403	.5416	.5428
3.5	.5441	.5453	.5465	.5478	.5490	.5502	.5514	.5527	.5539	.5551
3.6	.5563	.5575	.5587	.5599	.5611	.5623	.5635	.5647	.5658	.5670
3.7	.5682	.5694	.5705	.5717	.5729	.5740	.5752	.5763	.5775	.5786
3.8	.5798	.5809	.5821	.5832	.5843	.5855	.5866	.5877	.5888	.5899
3.9	.5911	.5922	.5933	.5944	.5955	.5966	.5977	.5988	.5999	.6010
4.0	.6021	.6031	.6042	.6053	.6064	.6075	.6085	.6096	.6107	.6117
4.1	.6128	.6138	.6149	.6160	.6170	.6180	.6191	.6201	.6212	.6222
4.2	.6232	.6243	.6253	.6263	.6274	.6284	.6294	.6304	.6314	.6325
4.3	.6335	.6345	.6355	.6365	.6375	.6385	.6395	.6405	.6415	.6425
4.4	.6435	.6444	.6454	.6464	.6474	.6484	.6493	.6503	.6513	.6522
4.5	.6532	.6542	.6551	.6561	.6571	.6580	.6590	.6599	.6609	.6618
4.6	.6628	.6637	.6646	.6656	.6665	.6675	.6684	.6693	.6702	.6712
4.7	.6721	.6730	.6739	.6749	.6758	.6767	.6776	.6785	.6794	.6803
4.8	.6812	.6821	.6830	.6839	.6848	.6857	.6866	.6875	.6884	.6893
4.9	.6902	.6911	.6920	.6928	.6937	.6946	.6955	.6964	.6972	.6981
5.0	.6990	.6998	.7007	.7016	.7024	.7033	.7042	.7050	.7059	.7067
5.1	.7076	.7084	.7093	.7101	.7110	.7118	.7126	.7135	.7143	.7152
5.2	.7160	.7168	.7177	.7185	.7193	.7202	.7210	.7218	.7226	.7235
5.3	.7243	.7251	.7259	.7267	.7275	.7284	.7292	.7300	.7308	.7316
5.4	.7324	.7332	.7340	.7348	.7356	.7364	.7372	.7380	.7388	.7396
N	0	1	2	3	4	5	6	7	8	9

TABLE II (Continued)
Logarithms of Numbers

N	0	1	2	3	4	5	6	7	8	9
5.5	.7404	.7412	.7419	.7427	.7435	.7443	.7451	.7459	.7466	.7474
5.6	.7482	.7490	.7497	.7505	.7513	.7520	.7528	.7536	.7543	.7551
5.7	.7559	.7566	.7574	.7582	.7589	.7597	.7604	.7612	.7619	.7627
5.8	.7634	.7642	.7649	.7657	.7664	.7672	.7679	.7686	.7694	.7701
5.9	.7709	.7716	.7723	.7731	.7738	.7745	.7752	.7760	.7767	.7774
6.0	.7782	.7789	.7796	.7803	.7810	.7818	.7825	.7832	.7839	.7846
6.1	.7853	.7860	.7868	.7875	.7882	.7889	.7896	.7903	.7910	.7917
6.2	.7924	.7931	.7938	.7945	.7952	.7959	.7966	.7973	.7980	.7987
6.3	.7993	.8000	.8007	.8014	.8021	.8028	.8035	.8041	.8048	.8055
6.4	.8062	.8069	.8075	.8082	.8089	.8096	.8102	.8109	.8116	.8122
6.5	.8129	.8136	.8142	.8149	.8156	.8162	.8169	.8176	.8182	.8189
6.6	.8195	.8202	.8209	.8215	.8222	.8228	.8235	.8241	.8248	.8254
6.7	.8261	.8267	.8274	.8280	.8287	.8293	.8299	.8306	.8312	.8319
6.8	.8325	.8331	.8338	.8344	.8351	.8357	.8363	.8370	.8376	.8382
6.9	.8388	.8395	.8401	.8407	.8414	.8420	.8426	.8432	.8439	.8445
7.0	.8451	.8457	.8463	.8470	.8476	.8482	.8488	.8494	.8500	.8506
7.1	.8513	.8519	.8525	.8531	.8537	.8543	.8549	.8555	.8561	.8567
7.2	.8573	.8579	.8585	.8591	.8597	.8603	.8609	.8615	.8621	.8627
7.3	.8633	.8639	.8645	.8651	.8657	.8663	.8669	.8675	.8681	.8686
7.4	.8692	.8698	.8704	.8710	.8716	.8722	.8727	.8733	.8739	.8745
7.5	.8751	.8756	.8762	.8768	.8774	.8779	.8785	.8791	.8797	.8802
7.6	.8808	.8814	.8820	.8825	.8831	.8837	.8842	.8848	.8854	.8859
7.7	.8865	.8871	.8876	.8882	.8887	.8893	.8899	.8904	.8910	.8915
7.8	.8921	.8927	.8932	.8938	.8943	.8949	.8954	.8960	.8965	.8971
7.9	.8976	.8982	.8987	.8993	.8998	.9004	.9009	.9015	.9020	.9025
8.0	.9031	.9036	.9042	.9047	.9053	.9058	.9063	.9069	.9074	.9079
8.1	.9085	.9090	.9096	.9101	.9106	.9112	.9117	.9122	.9128	.9133
8.2	.9138	.9143	.9149	.9154	.9159	.9165	.9170	.9175	.9180	.9186
8.3	.9191	.9196	.9201	.9206	.9212	.9217	.9222	.9227	.9232	.9238
8.4	.9243	.9248	.9253	.9258	.9263	.9269	.9274	.9279	.9284	.9289
8.5	.9294	.9299	.9304	.9309	.9315	.9320	.9325	.9330	.9335	.9340
8.6	.9345	.9350	.9355	.9360	.9365	.9370	.9375	.9380	.9385	.9390
8.7	.9395	.9400	.9405	.9410	.9415	.9420	.9425	.9430	.9435	.9440
8.8	.9445	.9450	.9455	.9460	.9465	.9469	.9474	.9479	.9484	.9489
8.9	.9494	.9499	.9504	.9509	.9513	.9518	.9523	.9528	.9533	.9538
9.0	.9542	.9547	.9552	.9557	.9562	.9566	.9571	.9576	.9581	.9586
9.1	.9590	.9595	.9600	.9605	.9609	.9614	.9619	.9624	.9628	.9633
9.2	.9638	.9643	.9647	.9652	.9657	.9661	.9666	.9671	.9675	.9680
9.3	.9685	.9689	.9694	.9699	.9703	.9708	.9713	.9717	.9722	.9727
9.4	.9731	.9736	.9741	.9745	.9750	.9754	.9759	.9763	.9768	.9773
9.5	.9777	.9782	.9786	.9791	.9795	.9800	.9805	.9809	.9814	.9818
9.6	.9823	.9827	.9832	.9836	.9841	.9845	.9850	.9854	.9859	.9863
9.7	.9868	.9872	.9877	.9881	.9886	.9890	.9894	.9899	.9903	.9908
9.8	.9912	.9917	.9921	.9926	.9930	.9934	.9939	.9943	.9948	.9952
9.9	.9956	.9961	.9965	.9969	.9974	.9978	.9983	.9987	.9991	.9996
N	0	1	2	3	4	5	6	7	8	9

TABLE III
148
Logarithms of Trigonometric Functions

Degrees	Log₁₀ Sine	Log₁₀ Tangent	Log₁₀ Cotangent	Log₁₀ Cosine	
0° 00′					90° 00′
10′	.4637 −3	.4637 −3	2.5363	.0000	50′
20′	.7648 −3	.7648 −3	2.2352	.0000	40′
30′	9408 −3	.9409 −3	2.0591	.0000	30′
40′	.0658 −2	.0658 −2	1.9342	.0000	20′
50′	.1627 −2	.1627 −2	1.8373	.0000	10′
1° 00′	.2419 −2	.2419 −2	1.7581	.9999 −1	89° 00′
10′	.3088 −2	.3089 −2	1.6911	.9999 −1	50′
20′	.3668 −2	.3669 −2	1.6331	.9999 −1	40′
30′	.4179 −2	.4181 −2	1.5819	.9999 −1	30′
40′	.4637 −2	.4638 −2	1.5362	.9998 −1	20′
50′	.5050 −2	.5053 −2	1.4947	.9998 −1	10′
2° 00′	.5428 −2	.5431 −2	1.4569	.9997 −1	88° 00′
10′	.5776 −2	.5779 −2	1.4221	.9997 −1	50′
20′	.6097 −2	.6101 −2	1.3899	.9996 −1	40′
30′	.6397 −2	.6401 −2	1.3599	.9996 −1	30′
40′	.6677 −2	.6682 −2	1.3318	.9995 −1	20′
50′	.6940 −2	.6945 −2	1.3055	.9995 −1	10′
3° 00′	.7188 −2	.7194 −2	1.2806	.9994 −1	87° 00′
10′	.7423 −2	.7429 −2	1.2571	.9993 −1	50′
20′	.7645 −2	.7652 −2	1.2348	.9993 −1	40′
30′	.7857 −2	.7865 −2	1.2135	.9992 −1	30′
40′	.8059 −2	.8067 −2	1.1933	.9991 −1	20′
50′	.8251 −2	.8261 −2	1.1739	.9990 −1	10′
4° 00′	.8436 −2	.8446 −2	1.1554	.9989 −1	86° 00′
10′	.8613 −2	.8624 −2	1.1376	.9989 −1	50′
20′	.8783 −2	.8795 −2	1.1205	.9988 −1	40′
30′	.8946 −2	.8960 −2	1.1040	.9987 −1	30′
40′	.9104 −2	.9118 −2	1.0882	.9986 −1	20′
50′	.9256 −2	.9272 −2	1.0728	.9985 −1	10′
5° 00′	.9403 −2	.9420 −2	1.0580	.9983 −1	85° 00′
10′	.9545 −2	.9563 −2	1.0437	.9982 −1	50′
20′	.9682 −2	.9701 −2	1.0299	.9981 −1	40′
30′	.9816 −2	.9836 −2	1.0164	.9980 −1	30′
40′	.9945 −2	.9966 −2	1.0034	.9979 −1	20′
50′	.0070 −1	.0093 −1	.9907	.9977 −1	10′
6° 00′	.0192 −1	.0216 −1	.9784	.9976 −1	84° 00′
10′	.0311 −1	.0336 −1	.9664	.9975 −1	50′
20′	.0426 −1	.0453 −1	.9547	.9973 −1	40′
30′	.0539 −1	.0567 −1	.9433	.9972 −1	30′
40′	.0648 −1	.0678 −1	.9322	.9971 −1	20′
50′	.0755 −1	.0786 −1	.9214	.9969 −1	10′
7° 00′	.0859 −1	.0891 −1	.9109	.9968 −1	83° 00′
10′	.0961 −1	.0995 −1	.9005	.9966 −1	50′
20′	.1060 −1	.1096 −1	.8904	.9964 −1	40′
30′	.1157 −1	.1194 −1	.8806	.9963 −1	30′
40′	.1252 −1	.1291 −1	.8709	.9961 −1	20′
50′	.1345 −1	.1385 −1	.8615	.9959 −1	10′
8° 00′	.1436 −1	.1478 −1	.8522	.9958 −1	82° 00′
10′	.1525 −1	.1569 −1	.8431	.9956 −1	50′
20′	.1612 −1	.1658 −1	.8342	.9954 −1	40′
30′	.1697 −1	.1745 −1	.8255	.9952 −1	30′
40′	.1781 −1	.1831 −1	.8169	.9950 −1	20′
50′	.1863 −1	.1915 −1	.8085	.9948 −1	10′
9° 00′	.1943 −1	.1997 −1	.8003	.9946 −1	81° 00′
	Log₁₀ Cosine	Log₁₀ Cotangent	Log₁₀ Tangent	Log₁₀ Sine	Degrees

TABLE III (Continued)
Logarithms of Trigonometric Functions

Degrees	Log₁₀ Sine	Log₁₀ Tangent	Log₁₀ Cotangent	Log₁₀ Cosine	
9° 00′	.1943 − 1	.1997 − 1	.8003	.9946 − 1	81° 00′
10′	.2022 − 1	.2078 − 1	.7922	.9944 − 1	50′
20′	.2100 − 1	.2158 − 1	.7842	.9942 − 1	40′
30′	.2176 − 1	.2236 − 1	.7764	.9940 − 1	30′
40′	.2251 − 1	.2313 − 1	.7687	.9938 − 1	20′
50′	.2324 − 1	.2389 − 1	.7611	.9936 − 1	10′
10° 00′	.2397 − 1	.2463 − 1	.7537	.9934 − 1	80° 00′
10′	.2468 − 1	.2536 − 1	.7464	.9931 − 1	50′
20′	.2538 − 1	.2609 − 1	.7391	.9929 − 1	40′
30′	.2606 − 1	.2680 − 1	.7320	.9927 − 1	30′
40′	.2674 − 1	.2750 − 1	.7250	.9924 − 1	20′
50′	.2740 − 1	.2819 − 1	.7181	.9922 − 1	10′
11° 00′	.2806 − 1	.2887 − 1	.7113	.9919 − 1	79° 00′
10′	.2870 − 1	.2953 − 1	.7047	.9917 − 1	50′
20′	.2934 − 1	.3020 − 1	.6980	.9914 − 1	40′
30′	.2997 − 1	.3085 − 1	.6915	.9912 − 1	30′
40′	.3058 − 1	.3149 − 1	.6851	.9909 − 1	20′
50′	.3119 − 1	.3212 − 1	.6788	.9907 − 1	10′
12° 00′	.3179 − 1	.3275 − 1	.6725	.9904 − 1	78° 00′
10′	.3238 − 1	.3336 − 1	.6664	.9901 − 1	50′
20′	.3296 − 1	.3397 − 1	.6603	.9899 − 1	40′
30′	.3353 − 1	.3458 − 1	.6542	.9896 − 1	30′
40′	.3410 − 1	.3517 − 1	.6483	.9893 − 1	20′
50′	.3466 − 1	.3576 − 1	.6424	.9890 − 1	10′
13° 00′	.3521 − 1	.3634 − 1	.6366	.9887 − 1	77° 00′
10′	.3575 − 1	.3691 − 1	.6309	.9884 − 1	50′
20′	.3629 − 1	.3748 − 1	.6252	.9881 − 1	40′
30′	.3682 − 1	.3804 − 1	.6196	.9878 − 1	30′
40′	.3734 − 1	.3859 − 1	.6141	.9875 − 1	20′
50′	.3786 − 1	.3914 − 1	.6086	.9872 − 1	10′
14° 00′	.3837 − 1	.3968 − 1	.6032	.9869 − 1	76° 00′
10′	.3887 − 1	.4021 − 1	.5979	.9866 − 1	50′
20′	.3937 − 1	.4074 − 1	.5926	.9863 − 1	40′
30′	.3986 − 1	.4127 − 1	.5873	.9859 − 1	30′
40′	.4035 − 1	.4178 − 1	.5822	.9856 − 1	20′
50′	.4083 − 1	.4230 − 1	.5770	.9853 − 1	10′
15° 00′	.4130 − 1	.4281 − 1	.5719	.9849 − 1	75° 00′
10′	.4177 − 1	.4331 − 1	.5669	.9846 − 1	50′
20′	.4223 − 1	.4381 − 1	.5619	.9843 − 1	40′
30′	.4269 − 1	.4430 − 1	.5570	.9839 − 1	30′
40′	.4314 − 1	.4479 − 1	.5521	.9836 − 1	20′
50′	.4359 − 1	.4527 − 1	.5473	.9832 − 1	10′
16° 00′	.4403 − 1	.4575 − 1	.5425	.9828 − 1	74° 00′
10′	.4447 − 1	.4622 − 1	.5378	.9825 − 1	50′
20′	.4491 − 1	.4669 − 1	.5331	.9821 − 1	40′
30′	.4533 − 1	.4716 − 1	.5284	.9817 − 1	30′
40′	.4576 − 1	.4762 − 1	.5238	.9814 − 1	20′
50′	.4618 − 1	.4808 − 1	.5192	.9810 − 1	10′
17° 00′	.4659 − 1	.4853 − 1	.5147	.9806 − 1	73° 00′
10′	.4700 − 1	.4898 − 1	.5102	.9802 − 1	50′
20′	.4741 − 1	.4943 − 1	.5057	.9798 − 1	40′
30′	.4781 − 1	.4987 − 1	.5013	.9794 − 1	30′
40′	.4821 − 1	.5031 − 1	.4969	.9790 − 1	20′
50′	.4861 − 1	.5075 − 1	.4925	.9786 − 1	10′
18° 00′	.4900 − 1	.5118 − 1	.4882	.9782 − 1	72° 00′
	Log₁₀ Cosine	Log₁₀ Cotangent	Log₁₀ Tangent	Log₁₀ Sine	Degrees

TABLE III (Continued)
Logarithms of Trigonometric Functions

Degrees	Log₁₀ Sine	Log₁₀ Tangent	Log₁₀ Cotangent	Log₁₀ Cosine	
18° 00′	.4900 − 1	.5118 − 1	.4882	.9782 − 1	72° 00′
10′	.4939 − 1	.5161 − 1	.4839	.9778 − 1	50′
20′	.4977 − 1	.5203 − 1	.4797	.9774 − 1	40′
30′	.5015 − 1	.5245 − 1	.4755	.9770 − 1	30′
40′	.5052 − 1	.5287 − 1	.4713	.9765 − 1	20′
50′	.5090 − 1	.5329 − 1	.4671	.9761 − 1	10′
19° 00′	.5126 − 1	.5370 − 1	.4630	.9757 − 1	71° 00′
10′	.5163 − 1	.5411 − 1	.4589	.9752 − 1	50′
20′	.5199 − 1	.5451 − 1	.4549	.9748 − 1	40′
30′	.5235 − 1	.5491 − 1	.4509	.9743 − 1	30′
40′	.5270 − 1	.5531 − 1	.4469	.9739 − 1	20′
50′	.5306 − 1	.5571 − 1	.4429	.9734 − 1	10′
20° 00′	.5341 − 1	.5611 − 1	.4389	.9730 − 1	70° 00′
10′	.5375 − 1	.5650 − 1	.4350	.9725 − 1	50′
20′	.5409 − 1	.5689 − 1	.4311	.9721 − 1	40′
30′	.5443 − 1	.5727 − 1	.4273	.9716 − 1	30′
40′	.5477 − 1	.5766 − 1	.4234	.9711 − 1	20′
50′	.5510 − 1	.5804 − 1	.4196	.9706 − 1	10′
21° 00′	.5543 − 1	.5842 − 1	.4158	.9702 − 1	69° 00′
10′	.5576 − 1	.5879 − 1	.4121	.9697 − 1	50′
20′	.5609 − 1	.5917 − 1	.4083	.9692 − 1	40′
30′	.5641 − 1	.5954 − 1	.4046	.9687 − 1	30′
40′	.5673 − 1	.5991 − 1	.4009	.9682 − 1	20′
50′	.5704 − 1	.6028 − 1	.3972	.9677 − 1	10′
22° 00′	.5736 − 1	.6064 − 1	.3936	.9672 − 1	68° 00′
10′	.5767 − 1	.6100 − 1	.3900	.9667 − 1	50′
20′	.5798 − 1	.6136 − 1	.3864	.9661 − 1	40′
30′	.5828 − 1	.6172 − 1	.3828	.9656 − 1	30′
40′	.5859 − 1	.6208 − 1	.3792	.9651 − 1	20′
50′	.5889 − 1	.6243 − 1	.3757	.9646 − 1	10′
23° 00′	.5919 − 1	.6279 − 1	.3721	.9640 − 1	67° 00′
10′	.5948 − 1	.6314 − 1	.3686	.9635 − 1	50′
20′	.5978 − 1	.6348 − 1	.3652	.9629 − 1	40′
30′	.6007 − 1	.6383 − 1	.3617	.9624 − 1	30′
40′	.6036 − 1	.6417 − 1	.3583	.9618 − 1	20′
50′	.6065 − 1	.6452 − 1	.3548	.9613 − 1	10′
24° 00′	.6093 − 1	.6486 − 1	.3514	.9607 − 1	66° 00′
10′	.6121 − 1	.6520 − 1	.3480	.9602 − 1	50′
20′	.6149 − 1	.6553 − 1	.3447	.9596 − 1	40′
30′	.6177 − 1	.6587 − 1	.3413	.9590 − 1	30′
40′	.6205 − 1	.6620 − 1	.3380	.9584 − 1	20′
50′	.6232 − 1	.6654 − 1	.3346	.9579 − 1	10′
25° 00′	.6259 − 1	.6687 − 1	.3313	.9573 − 1	65° 00′
10′	.6286 − 1	.6720 − 1	.3280	.9567 − 1	50′
20′	.6313 − 1	.6752 − 1	.3248	.9561 − 1	40′
30′	.6340 − 1	.6785 − 1	.3215	.9555 − 1	30′
40′	.6366 − 1	.6817 − 1	.3183	.9549 − 1	20′
50′	.6392 − 1	.6850 − 1	.3150	.9543 − 1	10′
26° 00′	.6418 − 1	.6882 − 1	.3118	.9537 − 1	64° 00′
10′	.6444 − 1	.6914 − 1	.3086	.9530 − 1	50′
20′	.6470 − 1	.6946 − 1	.3054	.9524 − 1	40′
30′	.6495 − 1	.6977 − 1	.3023	.9518 − 1	30′
40′	.6521 − 1	.7009 − 1	.2991	.9512 − 1	20′
50′	.6546 − 1	.7040 − 1	.2960	.9505 − 1	10′
27° 00′	.6570 − 1	.7072 − 1	.2928	.9499 − 1	63° 00′
	Log₁₀ Cosine	Log₁₀ Cotangent	Log₁₀ Tangent	Log₁₀ Sine	Degrees

TABLE III (Continued)

Logarithms of Trigonometric Functions

Degrees	Log₁₀ Sine	Log₁₀ Tangent	Log₁₀ Cotangent	Log₁₀ Cosine	
27° 00′	.6570 − 1	.7072 − 1	.2928	.9499 − 1	63° 00′
10′	.6595 − 1	.7103 − 1	.2897	.9492 − 1	50′
20′	.6620 − 1	.7134 − 1	.2866	.9486 − 1	40′
30′	.6644 − 1	.7165 − 1	.2835	.9479 − 1	30′
40′	.6668 − 1	.7196 − 1	.2804	.9473 − 1	20′
50′	.6692 − 1	.7226 − 1	.2774	.9466 − 1	10′
28° 00′	.6716 − 1	.7257 − 1	.2743	.9459 − 1	62° 00′
10′	.6740 − 1	.7287 − 1	.2713	.9453 − 1	50′
20′	.6763 − 1	.7317 − 1	.2683	.9446 − 1	40′
30′	.6787 − 1	.7348 − 1	.2652	.9439 − 1	30′
40′	.6810 − 1	.7378 − 1	.2622	.9432 − 1	20′
50′	.6833 − 1	.7408 − 1	.2592	.9425 − 1	10′
29° 00′	.6856 − 1	.7438 − 1	.2562	.9418 − 1	61° 00′
10′	.6878 − 1	.7467 − 1	.2533	.9411 − 1	50′
20′	.6901 − 1	.7497 − 1	.2503	.9404 − 1	40′
30′	.6923 − 1	.7526 − 1	.2474	.9397 − 1	30′
40′	.6946 − 1	.7556 − 1	.2444	.9390 − 1	20′
50′	.6968 − 1	.7585 − 1	.2415	.9383 − 1	10′
30° 00′	.6990 − 1	.7614 − 1	.2386	.9375 − 1	60° 00′
10′	.7012 − 1	.7644 − 1	.2356	.9368 − 1	50′
20′	.7033 − 1	.7673 − 1	.2327	.9361 − 1	40′
30′	.7055 − 1	.7701 − 1	.2299	.9353 − 1	30′
40′	.7076 − 1	.7730 − 1	.2270	.9346 − 1	20′
50′	.7097 − 1	.7759 − 1	.2241	.9338 − 1	10′
31° 00′	.7118 − 1	.7788 − 1	.2212	.9331 − 1	59° 00′
10′	.7139 − 1	.7816 − 1	.2184	.9323 − 1	50′
20′	.7160 − 1	.7845 − 1	.2155	.9315 − 1	40′
30′	.7181 − 1	.7873 − 1	.2127	.9308 − 1	30′
40′	.7201 − 1	.7902 − 1	.2098	.9300 − 1	20′
50′	.7222 − 1	.7930 − 1	.2070	.9292 − 1	10′
32° 00′	.7242 − 1	.7958 − 1	.2042	.9284 − 1	58° 00′
10′	.7262 − 1	.7986 − 1	.2014	.9276 − 1	50′
20′	.7282 − 1	.8014 − 1	.1986	.9268 − 1	40′
30′	.7302 − 1	.8042 − 1	.1958	.9260 − 1	30′
40′	.7322 − 1	.8070 − 1	.1930	.9252 − 1	20′
50′	.7342 − 1	.8097 − 1	.1903	.9244 − 1	10′
33° 00′	.7361 − 1	.8125 − 1	.1875	.9236 − 1	57° 00′
10′	.7380 − 1	.8153 − 1	.1847	.9228 − 1	50′
20′	.7400 − 1	.8180 − 1	.1820	.9219 − 1	40′
30′	.7419 − 1	.8208 − 1	.1792	.9211 − 1	30′
40′	.7438 − 1	.8235 − 1	.1765	.9203 − 1	20′
50′	.7457 − 1	.8263 − 1	.1737	.9194 − 1	10′
34° 00′	.7476 − 1	.8290 − 1	.1710	.9186 − 1	56° 00′
10′	.7494 − 1	.8317 − 1	.1683	.9177 − 1	50′
20′	.7513 − 1	.8344 − 1	.1656	.9169 − 1	40′
30′	.7531 − 1	.8371 − 1	.1629	.9160 − 1	30′
40′	.7550 − 1	.8398 − 1	.1602	.9151 − 1	20′
50′	.7568 − 1	.8425 − 1	.1575	.9142 − 1	10′
35° 00′	.7586 − 1	.8452 − 1	.1548	.9134 − 1	55° 00′
10′	.7604 − 1	.8479 − 1	.1521	.9125 − 1	50′
20′	.7622 − 1	.8506 − 1	.1494	.9116 − 1	40′
30′	.7640 − 1	.8533 − 1	.1467	.9107 − 1	30′
40′	.7657 − 1	.8559 − 1	.1441	.9098 − 1	20′
50′	.7675 − 1	.8586 − 1	.1414	.9089 − 1	10′
36° 00′	.7692 − 1	.8613 − 1	.1387	.9080 − 1	54° 00′
	Log₁₀ Cosine	Log₁₀ Cotangent	Log₁₀ Tangent	Log₁₀ Sine	Degrees

TABLE III (Continued)
Logarithms of Trigonometric Functions

Degrees	Log₁₀ Sine	Log₁₀ Tangent	Log₁₀ Cotangent	Log₁₀ Cosine	
36° 00′	.7692 −1	.8613 −1	.1387	.9080 −1	54° 00′
10′	.7710 −1	.8639 −1	.1361	.9070 −1	50′
20′	.7727 −1	.8666 −1	.1334	.9061 −1	40′
30′	.7744 −1	.8692 −1	.1308	.9052 −1	30′
40′	.7761 −1	.8718 −1	.1282	.9042 −1	20′
50′	.7778 −1	.8745 −1	.1255	.9033 −1	10′
37° 00′	.7795 −1	.8771 −1	.1229	.9023 −1	53° 00′
10′	.7811 −1	.8797 −1	.1203	.9014 −1	50′
20′	.7828 −1	.8824 −1	.1176	.9004 −1	40′
30′	.7844 −1	.8850 −1	.1150	.8995 −1	30′
40′	.7861 −1	.8876 −1	.1124	.8985 −1	20′
50′	.7877 −1	.8902 −1	.1098	.8975 −1	10′
38° 00′	.7893 −1	.8928 −1	.1072	.8965 −1	52° 00′
10′	.7910 −1	.8954 −1	.1046	.8955 −1	50′
20′	.7926 −1	.8980 −1	.1020	.8945 −1	40′
30′	.7941 −1	.9006 −1	.0994	.8935 −1	30′
40′	.7957 −1	.9032 −1	.0968	.8925 −1	20′
50′	.7973 −1	.9058 −1	.0942	.8915 −1	10′
39° 00′	.7989 −1	.9084 −1	.0916	.8905 −1	51° 00′
10′	.8004 −1	.9110 −1	.0890	.8895 −1	50′
20′	.8020 −1	.9135 −1	.0865	.8884 −1	40′
30′	.8035 −1	.9161 −1	.0839	.8874 −1	30′
40′	.8050 −1	.9187 −1	.0813	.8864 −1	20′
50′	.8066 −1	.9212 −1	.0788	.8853 −1	10′
40° 00′	.8081 −1	.9238 −1	.0762	.8843 −1	50° 00′
10′	.8096 −1	.9264 −1	.0736	.8832 −1	50′
20′	.8111 −1	.9289 −1	.0711	.8821 −1	40′
30′	.8125 −1	.9315 −1	.0685	.8810 −1	30′
40′	.8140 −1	.9341 −1	.0659	.8800 −1	20′
50′	.8155 −1	.9366 −1	.0634	.8789 −1	10′
41° 00′	.8169 −1	.9392 −1	.0608	.8778 −1	49° 00′
10′	.8184 −1	.9417 −1	.0583	.8767 −1	50′
20′	.8198 −1	.9443 −1	.0557	.8756 −1	40′
30′	.8213 −1	.9468 −1	.0532	.8745 −1	30′
40′	.8227 −1	.9494 −1	.0506	.8733 −1	20′
50′	.8241 −1	.9519 −1	.0481	.8722 −1	10′
42° 00′	.8255 −1	.9544 −1	.0456	.8711 −1	48° 00′
10′	.8269 −1	.9570 −1	.0430	.8699 −1	50′
20′	.8283 −1	.9595 −1	.0405	.8688 −1	40′
30′	.8297 −1	.9621 −1	.0379	.8676 −1	30′
40′	.8311 −1	.9646 −1	.0354	.8665 −1	20′
50′	.8324 −1	.9671 −1	.0329	.8653 −1	10′
43° 00′	.8338 −1	.9697 −1	.0303	.8641 −1	47° 00′
10′	.8351 −1	.9722 −1	.0278	.8629 −1	50′
20′	.8365 −1	.9747 −1	.0253	.8618 −1	40′
30′	.8378 −1	.9772 −1	.0228	.8606 −1	30′
40′	.8391 −1	.9798 −1	.0202	.8594 −1	20′
50′	.8405 −1	.9823 −1	.0177	.8582 −1	10′
44° 00′	.8418 −1	.9848 −1	.0152	.8569 −1	46° 00′
10′	.8431 −1	.9874 −1	.0126	.8557 −1	50′
20′	.8444 −1	.9899 −1	.0101	.8545 −1	40′
30′	.8457 −1	.9924 −1	.0076	.8532 −1	30′
40′	.8469 −1	.9949 −1	.0051	.8520 −1	20′
50′	.8482 −1	.9975 −1	.0025	.8507 −1	10′
45° 00′	.8495 −1	.0000	.0000	.8495 −1	45° 00′
	Log₁₀ Cosine	Log₁₀ Cotangent	Log₁₀ Tangent	Log₁₀ Sine	Degrees

TABLE IV

Powers and Roots

No.	Sq.	Sq. Root	Cube	Cube Root	No.	Sq.	Sq. Root	Cube	Cube Root
1	1	1.000	1	1.000	51	2,601	7.141	132,651	3.708
2	4	1.414	8	1.260	52	2,704	7.211	140,608	3.733
3	9	1.732	27	1.442	53	2,809	7.280	148,877	3.756
4	16	2.000	64	1.587	54	2,916	7.348	157,464	3.780
5	25	2.236	125	1.710	55	3,025	7.416	166,375	3.803
6	36	2.449	216	1.817	56	3,136	7.483	175,616	3.826
7	49	2.646	343	1.913	57	3,249	7.550	185,193	3.849
8	64	2.828	512	2.000	58	3,364	7.616	195,112	3.871
9	81	3.000	729	2.080	59	3,481	7.681	205,379	3.893
10	100	3.162	1,000	2.154	60	3,600	7.746	216,000	3.915
11	121	3.317	1,331	2.224	61	3,721	7.810	226,981	3.936
12	144	3.464	1,728	2.289	62	3,844	7.874	238,328	3.958
13	169	3.606	2,197	2.351	63	3,969	7.937	250,047	3.979
14	196	3.742	2,744	2.410	64	4,096	8.000	262,144	4.000
15	225	3.873	3,375	2.466	65	4,225	8.062	274,625	4.021
16	256	4.000	4,096	2.520	66	4,356	8.124	287,496	4.041
17	289	4.123	4,913	2.571	67	4,489	8.185	300,763	4.062
18	324	4.243	5,832	2.621	68	4,624	8.246	314,432	4.082
19	361	4.359	6,859	2.668	69	4,761	8.307	328,509	4.102
20	400	4.472	8,000	2.714	70	4,900	8.367	343,000	4.121
21	441	4.583	9,261	2.759	71	5,041	8.426	357,911	4.141
22	484	4.690	10,648	2.802	72	5,184	8.485	373,248	4.160
23	529	4.796	12,167	2.844	73	5,329	8.544	389,017	4.179
24	576	4.899	13,824	2.884	74	5,476	8.602	405,224	4.198
25	625	5.000	15,625	2.924	75	5,625	8.660	421,875	4.217
26	676	5.099	17,576	2.962	76	5,776	8.718	438,976	4.236
27	729	5.196	19,683	3.000	77	5,929	8.775	456,533	4.254
28	784	5.292	21,952	3.037	78	6,084	8.832	474,552	4.273
29	841	5.385	24,389	3.072	79	6,241	8.888	493,039	4.291
30	900	5.477	27,000	3.107	80	6,400	8.944	512,000	4.309
31	961	5.568	29,791	3.141	81	6,561	9.000	531,441	4.327
32	1,024	5.657	32,768	3.175	82	6,724	9.055	551,368	4.344
33	1,089	5.745	35,937	3.208	83	6,889	9.110	571,787	4.362
34	1,156	5.831	39,304	3.240	84	7,056	9.165	592,704	4.380
35	1,225	5.916	42,875	3.271	85	7,225	9.220	614,125	4.397
36	1,296	6.000	46,656	3.302	86	7,396	9.274	636,056	4.414
37	1,369	6.083	50,653	3.332	87	7,569	9.327	658,503	4.431
38	1,444	6.164	54,872	3.362	88	7,744	9.381	681,472	4.448
39	1,521	6.245	59,319	3.391	89	7,921	9.434	704,969	4.465
40	1,600	6.325	64,000	3.420	90	8,100	9.487	729,000	4.481
41	1,681	6.403	68,921	3.448	91	8,281	9.539	753,571	4.498
42	1,764	6.481	74,088	3.476	92	8,464	9.592	778,688	4.514
43	1,849	6.557	79,507	3.503	93	8,649	9.644	804,357	4.531
44	1,936	6.633	85,184	3.530	94	8,836	9.695	830,584	4.547
45	2,025	6.708	91,125	3.557	95	9,025	9.747	857,375	4.563
46	2,116	6.782	97,336	3.583	96	9,216	9.798	884,736	4.579
47	2,209	6.856	103,823	3.609	97	9,409	9.849	912,673	4.595
48	2,304	6.928	110,592	3.634	98	9,604	9.899	941,192	4.610
49	2,401	7.000	117,649	3.659	99	9,801	9.950	970,299	4.626
50	2,500	7.071	125,000	3.684	100	10,000	10.000	1,000,000	4.642

INDEX